Advance Praise for
IN THIS TOGETHER

Trammell Crow and Bill Shireman have developed a bold and courageous theory of change that rejects twentieth century Right/Left and Conservative/Progressive divisions and embraces an enlightened vision and achievable plan that are animated, not by our differences, but by our collective survival instincts, shared interests and common destinies, and that are passionately devoted to protecting the health and well-being of our planet while assuring that freedom, justice, Democracy and Capitalism thrive in the twenty-first century and beyond.

—Rob Stein, Cross-Partisan Strategist;
Founder, the Democracy Alliance

An overdue and powerful call for a post-partisan approach to climate, in which everyday conservatives and progressives join forces to ensure a sustainable future, together.

—Josh Silver, Co-founder & Executive Director,
RepresentUs

There's no reason why economic and environmental interests need to be at war. Both Shireman and Crow have done a tremendous amount to show exactly why and how what's good for the planet is also good for the economy.

—Eli Lehrer, President,
R Street Institute

Read this to be upset, confused, conflicted, excited and maybe even hopeful. Collaborating we can achieve amazing progress. Fighting we all lose.

—Joan Blades, Living Room Conversations on
Energy and Climate; co-founder, MoveOn.org

Crow and Shireman have made a convincing case that to make progress on climate change, we need a different incentive structure in politics. Imagine competing with the BEST plans to fuel political campaigns instead of divisive rhetoric. This requires us, the voters, to support problem solvers in a transpartisan way, which this book inspires us to do.

—Debilyn Molineaux, Co-Founder, Bridge Alliance
(BridgeAlliance.US)

Crow and Shireman highlight the true power of citizens when we break free from the thrall of the politics industry. Progress on climate change IS possible when we demand our elected officials work together to solve problems instead of using our problems to sow hate and division amongst us. The environment is one area where we surely can and must find common ground.

—David L. Nevins, Co-Founder, Bridge Alliance
(BridgeAlliance.US)

Thomas Edison once said that vision without execution is hallucination. Trammell Crow and Bill Shireman dispel a raft of political hallucinations and offer a bold and compelling way forward to address the climate crisis.

—Jerry Taylor, President, Niskanen Center

A Green Deal that Republicans and Democrats support won't be the much needed ecological u-turn, but it gets us started working together for a better world. Such a fundamental step will help us eventually revolutionize societal systems to be in sync with natural systems. Crow and Shireman's book needs to be widely read by the major political parties.

—Randy Hayes, Rainforest Action Network founder,
Executive Director of Foundation Earth

Climate change is not a political problem - objective science can help both parties find solutions that make sense. This book may be politically incorrect, but it comes at the right time, as it is increasingly clear that progress requires bold collaboration across the aisle.

—Elizabeth A. Muller, Executive Director of Berkeley Earth,
CEO of Deep Isolation

A Declaration of Interdependence
E Pluribus Unum

We're not all the same, but we are a family.

We don't always agree, but we are not at war.

From many, we are one, not in a melting pot, but a complex social fabric.

In a spirit of caring, connection, and creation, we embrace four principles:

- **No Enemies** – We work through our conflicts to find solutions.
- **No Denial** – We face facts, discuss our differences, and resolve them.
- **No Excuses** – We each do our part – every citizen, leader, and business.
- **No Delay** – We each take action together, now.

We are all in this together.
Our differences are part of us.
Together, we are whole.

Dear John & Katie,
Thanks for knowing what I've
been trying to say, even if I sound
crazy. NYT, WPost & LAT declined to publish,
& then Bill & Trammell gave me the last word.
Biggest hugs & LOVE ♡ M

IN THIS TOGETHER

HOW REPUBLICANS, DEMOCRATS, CAPITALISTS, AND ACTIVISTS ARE UNITING TO TACKLE CLIMATE CHANGE AND MORE.

TRAMMELL S. CROW
and BILL SHIREMAN

Printed in the United States of America

First Printing, 2020

ISBN 13: 978-0-9854524-9-0

Affinity Press
1 2 3 4 5 6 7 8 9 0

TEST YOUR
ECO-POLITICAL IQ

1. Which endangered North American political species, if allowed to go extinct, could lead to the end of the planet?

2. What industry is the biggest barrier to real climate solutions and earning obscene profits doing it? Hint: it's not coal, oil, gas, chemicals, or food. Not even fracking.

3. Why is the War on Climate Change a boon for vested interests, and a corporatist's and statist's dream?

4. Why is it self-defeating to demand climate action, and how can taking climate action succeed?

5. How could the Green New Deal backfire and deliver the opposite of what environmentalists envision? How can we make it work?

6. Why is one green Republican in Congress worth four to eight green Democrats?

7. How could an electoral Blue Wave or Red Wave doom us all? Why do we need support from the left and right?

8. Why can't we save the planet unless we save democracy?

9. How are crony capitalism and democratic socialism alike?

10. What is the going price to buy Congress if we want to save the planet? Are there financing opportunities for qualified buyers? Do climate activists qualify? And is a lease-to-own deal smarter?

11. Extra Credit: What can you do to save the planet—and freedom, justice, and liberal democracy too?

CONTENTS

FOREWORD

In This Together

By Mindy Finn and Rob Stein

Democracies throughout the world, including America, are experiencing increasing erosion of political cohesion. Hyper-partisanship is growing, effective governance is being blocked, and authoritarianism is rising.

The COVID-19 pandemic, and its profound health, economic, social, and political consequences, are exacerbating these dysfunctions.

In America, our current corrosive political climate, and the entrenched two-party political-industrial complex, are being driven by an aggressive, data-based, turbo-charged partisan duopoly that feeds on divisive and oppositional politics. Our civic life is coarsened by negative messages that are derived from partisan data engines owned by each of the party complexes and amplified by the incessant drumbeat of partisan cable and social media.

There is virtually no space in our national civic life for respectful dialogue, thoughtful deliberation, evidence-based problem-solving, civility in the public square, or effective governance.

Indeed, the health and vitality of our politics and our democracy are weakening.

We each have spent the majority of our professional lives in partisan politics: Mindy as a conservative Republican and Rob as a liberal Democrat. We deeply value our Nation's founding principles of freedom, justice, and opportunity for all. And, we are committed to the protection of democratic ideals, institutions and norms, evidence-based problem-solving, and greater civility in public life.

We love our country and believe our common needs and collective destiny are more important than party, ideology and special interests.

We met several years ago through a structured conversation known as Patriots and Pragmatists. It is a network of roughly 60 conservative and 60 liberal thought leaders, journalists, pundits, academics, organizational heads and donors. This remarkable alliance of thinkers, strategists, and operatives has created a safe space for people from across America's political and cultural spectrums to explore new ideas, strategies, and relationships focused on reducing hyper-partisanship and improving effective democratic governance.

We each joined this network because we are seeking fresh ways of thinking about our country's problems and are looking for new allies open to exploring philosophical and political commonalities across traditional divides instead of remaining mired in deepening political divisions.

We hunger for a new, cross-partisan cultural and political voice in America. And, therefore, we share a keen interest in the institutional scaffolding necessary to create a vibrant and sustainable voice for change in our country. The components of such an infrastructure include capacities to build a robust cross-partisan constituency of millions of Americans, a sophisticated cross-partisan data management and analytics engine, and the human and financial resources necessary to sustainably execute and finance an agenda for strengthening our democracy and renewing our civic life.

Our work with Trammell and Bill grew out of a meeting in April 2019 with their network of about a dozen of the nation's wealthiest Republican political donors. The topic of their gathering was what can Republicans do to help end climate denial and return the GOP to its historical legacy as an environmental problem-solver. At the meeting, Republican mega-donors sat at the table with conservative and liberal strategists sharing ideas, debating plans, trying to figure out how to stop partisanship from driving our democracy over the brink, and destroying the environment in the process.

We have participated in these conversations, not because we are experts on the environment or climate change, but because Trammell and Bill are committed to engaging an increasing number of wealthy Republican men and women, who care deeply about the health of our planet, in a larger conversation about how hyper-partisanship is precluding all of us from achieving any meaningful substantive solutions on virtually every topic.

We have shared with Trammell, Bill, and their colleagues the cross-partisan efforts that are underway to build a new voice in American culture and politics that is devoted not to party orthodoxies or special interests, but to solving complex twenty-first century problems. As former soldiers in our respective parties, we understand that so long as the allegiances and incentives are to divide our country, effective governance is stymied.

This is why an emerging cross-partisan community of Republicans, Democrats, and Independents are working together to support state-based electoral reforms, the election of open-minded Republicans and Democrats, and programs devoted to bridging differences, enhancing civic learning and cross-partisan problem-solving.

Key to this work, and to lessening the poisonous consequences of polarization, healing our democracy, and advancing progress on climate change—and to other issues of pressing national and global importance—is a commitment to building a cross-partisan constituency of ten million or more activists devoted to country, not party, and to amplifying and empowering its voice.

Sophisticated cross-partisan data, analytics, and tools for connecting us based on shared values and interests are indispensable to creating a new unifying voice in America's culture and politics.

America needs a new operating model for our politics and media, an *intentional* model designed by a new generation of cross-partisan political pioneers, who possess the same passions and spirit for *interdependence* as our Founders had for *independence*. With it, we can compete effectively with the existing hyper-partisan data duopoly to empower the rest of us—the 70% ready to find collaborative solutions on climate, education, infrastructure, and runaway debt at every level.

Trammell and Bill have developed a bold and courageous theory of change that rejects twentieth century right/left and conservative/ progressive tribal prejudices and embraces an enlightened vision and action plan animated by shared interests and common destinies. What animates this mission is a passionate devotion to protecting the health and well-being of our planet while assuring that the core values of democracy and capitalism—freedom, justice, and opportunity for all—thrive in the twenty-first century and beyond.

Our democracy is at a crossroads. In the pages of *In This Together* that follow, Trammell and Bill have crafted an achievable path forward to open minds, save our planet, heal our country and inspire a new American beginning. In the words of John Schnaar, they are encouraging us all to accept responsibility for creating a hopeful future:

> *"The future is not some place we are going,*
> *but one we are creating.*
> *The paths are not to be found, but made.*
> *And the activity of making them,*
> *changes both the maker and the destination."*

With Hope, Faith, and Appreciation to Trammell and Bill,

Mindy Finn
Rob Stein

PREFACE

We're endangered, but not extinct. We have time to think. It may seem like our race began around two centuries ago. But prior hominids passed us the baton 500,000 years ago, after carrying it for six million years, in a line of succession that stretches back past every phase and stage of creation, all the way to the beginning of time. This is not a sprint we're running, unless we're ready to finish the race, now. This is a long, long, long distance run, with so much to see along the way. We have time to experience it all, but only if we take it.

America is a part of the journey we're all on, a precious and exceptional part. America is far from perfect—stained from the start in our founding documents by bigotries not yet ready to succumb. We aren't just these documents - we come from something inside, beyond a place or a time. We are an idea, one with moral force deeper than we can know. Our idea didn't come from rich white European men. They were just simply carriers. They brought it from the ancient kings of Africa, the philosophers of the Middle East and Asia, the political theorists of the west and north, the founders of our revolutions here and abroad. Each one of us finds it inside of us. That idea is not power or prosperity, though they can be useful enablers and welcome rewards. The idea is freedom—freedom to discover and reveal everything in our nature, and the opportunity, with wisdom, to treat her well.

Her best days, and ours, are ahead.

We are an endangered political species—pro-environment fiscally conservative Republicans. We embrace the radical idea that freedom, prosperity, and a healthy environment are not just compatible, but inseparable. And we need your help.

Tens of millions of us used to roam North America freely, criss-crossing every state and province, helping purify the nation's air and water, conserving open space, repairing the ozone layer, and spreading prosperity by assuring that polluters pay a price.

But in the past generation, our numbers have been decimated by poachers determined to eliminate every genetic trace of us from the Republican Party.

These ideological warriors are passionate, and their motivations are mostly pure. They have ideals they believe in, and fears that are real. But they are being used, just as their progressive counterparts are, in a war against the ideals they think they're fighting for.

You can stop the slaughter. Not by firing back at the right-wing warriors hunting us, but by hearing their words, understanding their fears, then speaking to the millions ready to end this war and save the planet.

Fed up with the war, a new constituency is forming in between the battling tribes, a reconstruction of the mainstream right and left with the potential to depolarize and revitalize democracy.

The two of us are a part of that constituency. We are determined to help activate it. Perhaps you are too. With principled scholars and strategists, we and our colleagues have spent nearly ten years and over $80 million learning to identify, reach, and mobilize the growing base we call the Solution Citizens—the resolutionary one-in-five of us who can unite 70% of Americans behind solutions.

This book is part introduction, part agenda, and part strategy on how to save the planet from deniers on both the right and left. We introduce conservatives and progressives to each other, not as we've been caricatured, but more as we are: complementary opposites who need each other. We present an agenda to protect the planet that brings together the best of the left and right. And because this agenda—indeed any authentic green deal—is politically possible only with cross-partisan support, we propose a strategy to save the environment while we also preserve our prosperity and reclaim our democracy.

We problem-solvers are different from the warriors who get most of the attention in today's polarizing media. Warriors drive wedges between us, then build walls to keep us apart. We remove the wedges and break down the walls that separate Americans by racial, ethnic, and gender identity, and divide us over abortion guns, immigration, and climate.

Some problem-solvers are conservatives, some progressives, some libertarians, but our differences don't keep us apart—they bring us together in a whole greater than the sum of us. And we discover that as a community united by our complementarity, we hold the solutions to a host of unresolved problems now exploited to disempower us. We can fix our broken criminal justice system, upgrade our declining public schools, deliver superior health care we can all afford, narrow economic inequity, renew our deteriorating infrastructure, and restore opportunity and prosperity for the middle class.

But one issue unites us above all others. Our polls and campaigns prove it. From the left to the right, we want to protect the environment.

To problem-solvers, the environment is not just some thing to save. It is a whole system we depend on, for everything; a living system that is sacred and whole. We don't choose between a healthy environment and a prosperous economy. We understand these two are linked. Politicians want us to place them in opposition. We know how to bring them together.

So we celebrated, cautiously, when progressive Democrats stepped up in 2019 to propose a Green New Deal (GND). Finally, a proposal that's positive and visionary. Not that we support it as-is. It's more poetry than prose, inspiring for idealists, enticing for the entrenched. Vested interests would capture it too quickly. But its champions are right in one key respect: we can't attack our economic, social, and environmental problems separately, one at a time. We need a systemic approach that gets to the root cause of them all.

The GND can't possibly pass, Republican friends tell us. But in effect, it did so just as we were finishing this book. The $2.2 trillion Big Deal to reduce economic pain from COVID-19 is a mash-up collage of all the colors of the establishment rainbow, left and right. "We did this together," said House Minority Leader Kevin McCarthy after it passed almost by acclamation. House Speaker Nancy Pelosi called it "visionary" and "evidence-based."

But can a $2 trillion dollar package that hands out money in amounts rounded to the nearest $50 billion be evidence-based? The biggest flaw in the Big Deal, like the GND before it, is the absence of authentic Republican ideas—the ones the party used to stand for, the ones that can make government work. Forgive us for saying it, but the left needs the right, and vice-versa. When the two aren't insulting each other, we're quite complementary. Conservatives need progressives to help them envision what's possible. Progressives need conservatives to help them realize their vision. Conservatives know how to harness systems—like nature and free markets—to get the job done.

You might ask, *"if you have so much to contribute, where have you been?"* Frankly, we've been preoccupied with dodging bullets inside and outside our own tent. So have many of you.

Both the Republican and Democratic parties are wracked by civil war, as fundamentalists battle to rid each of the diverse people and ideas they find heretical, so they can unite in ideological purity to destroy the enemies of righteousness.

The result is two parties culled of diverse people and ideas, looking more like enormous focus groups of homogenous voters selected by professionals so their behavior can be even more finely tuned.

Conveniently, but not coincidentally, the demographic profile of the two parties seems tailor-made for political strategists who sell protection to vested interests and media professionals who hock advertising to the brands we buy to love. It's as if they've installed giant signs across America designating exactly where they need us all to stand:

Attention women, young, Hispanic, African-American, and college-educated professionals—please stand inside the chamber on the left, the one marked The Powerless. Once you're all inside, seal it shut so all you hear are the echoed reminders of your impotence and your enemy's power. We're custom-spinning your Google searches, Facebook homepage, MSNBC programming, and New York Times alerts to confirm your worst fears and foulest stereotypes about those people-not-like-us in the chamber on the right.

Attention men, older, whiter, and religious working-class Americans— please stand inside the chamber on the right, the one marked The Persecuted. Once you're all inside, seal it shut so all you hear are the echoes of how disrespected you are. We're hardwiring you to 24/7 Fox, Breitbart, Facebook, Google, and Wall Street Journal alarms to confirm your worst suspicions worries and validate your vile about the people-not-like-us in the chamber on the left.

The result is millions of Americans sorted according to our fears, hopes, weaknesses, and obsessions into digital concentration camps, making us ready targets for media marksmen looking for a clean shot.

Inside each camp is a minority of true-believing enforcers who keep the rest of us in line so we're easier to point, holler, and fire at. The Warriors are equipped with megaphones to call us out for any impermissible ideas or inadmissible facts we might entertain. The Warriors don't know it, but they are unpaid cast members in a made-for-multimedia reality show that sells the rest of us to the very corporate and state interest groups they think they're fighting.

So with this book, we hope to convey a truth that may not be self-evident. The battle between the left and right does not pit justice against freedom, people against profit, or corporatism against statism. It is, instead, a tool that the Republican and Democratic Duopoly uses to divert our attention from them. So long as we are either entertained by pablum or at war over politics, we can be sold to vested interests tapped into the national treasury and advertisers accessing their share of consumer spending.

Who should we blame most for the Duopoly distorting our democracy? Republicans or Democrats? Corporations or the state? Middle or coastal America? "Political power brokers or media marketers? Deep state managers or intellectual elites?" If you're asking that, you're not wrong, you just haven't been listening. All of us are being played, right or wrong. Finger-pointing is the name of the game, deserved or not. The Duopoly grabs every one of us and points our fingers angrily toward every big-asset institution we love to hate, keeping us enraged and our demons at risk so they can keep extracting money and power. Its strategic position gives it the power, if threatened, to rip off both the private and public parts of any corporation, union, military contractor, trade group, non-profit, or service provider that doesn't keep it fed and fat.

How can we outmaneuver an adversary that holds all our institutions hostage? It turns out there is a way. We will explain later how you and I, plus around five million of our friends, can take back democracy from the Duopoly, and stop liquidating our economic, social, and ecological assets.

Until we do, visionary legislation is only politically viable if it feeds the Duopoly. "What does that mean for the Big Deal rescue package? In the short term, it starves off collapse. But it will also be captured and turned into a corporatist's and a statist's dream—unless we on the right and left step outside our chambers, and join forces to work on it together.

Here's the reality. Politics is a business. It's managed by political and advertising professionals who grab millions of us by the eyeballs and thrust screens into our faces, where marketing messages flash before us while our conscious brains are caught off-guard.

The democracy industry and its two lead companies, which we'll call Democratic LLC and Republican LLC, extracts at least $6 billion a year from companies convinced they need to "protect" their good and bad investments, outmoded business models, and government contracts and paybacks from any threatening changes. It's a tiny investment, given its high return, since it buys them access to a public treasury that takes in over $3 trillion from us each year, and spends over $4 trillion. The extra trillion-plus gets tacked on to the national debt, so our kids can pay it "back" to our many global creditors.

But the democracy industry is tiny compared with our media companies. They skim $240 billion a year from companies who want access to us. That sounds like a lot, but again, it's worth it. It opens a gateway that gives advertisers access to over 329 million soft receptive brains, conditioned to respond to triggers, and to reliably part with around $14 trillion each year for goods and services that we have been convinced we desperately need.

Warriors on the left rail against this consumerism and the social and ecological havoc it wreaks. They know it's not their fault. It is, they would like to believe, all a conspiracy of big oil, big coal, Charles Koch, capitalism, or all-of-the-above. Warriors on the right are just as disparaging of this unholy materialism. They, however, think it's the Deep State, immigrants, George Soros, socialism, or all of them.

Many of their nemeses, left and right, are involved, of course. But the truth is, most of them are almost as trapped by the system as we are. They are the official demons placed in our field of view so we can't see the systemic root of the problem.

At its root, our endless political wars are declared and redeclared day after day, bit after bit, by what business leader Katherine Gehl and Harvard Business School Professor Michael Porter call the Duopoly.

The Duopoly is the interlocking complex of political and media strategists, message testers, pollsters, lobbyists, and ad-based news media that profit by dividing our body politic in two, and threatening to break the backbone of democracy..

We admit it—we'd like to blame the lobbyists and media for all our problems, but we can't. They're just the latest villains cast by a system that's so corrupted it doesn't need scoundrels to do its dirty work. Good people will do it just fine.

Consider the Green New Deal that progressive Democrats introduced in 2019. It began as poetry, a soaring expression of high expectations. But from day one it began its descent, as interest groups fell on lawmakers like Gollums on Precious, seeking cuts for themselves and their clients who promise to deliver what the people want. The GND itself will never go anywhere whole. It will be pieced out by well-connected clean tech, energy, food, agriculture, labor, health, and environmental interest groups will be drawn into a bidding war to see who can meet our demands for the most money—and in our pay-to-play political culture, it's the highest bidder who will win. Cheap and effective solutions will go nowhere—where's the money to grease the wheels? Expensive non-solutions will be loaded up with bait and signed into law. Quick high-visibility benefits will evidence their worth. Then, as our attention goes elsewhere, progress will slow, stop, and even reverse. A few years later, a new generation will be alarmed enough to start over. "Never again," they will declare, as they blame today's young people, who will be old, and demand action now.

It doesn't need to be that way. We need to stop demanding action, as if we're powerless.

Big corporations and big government prosper by making us feel dependent on them, but it's the other way around. They depend on us. We have the money, the muscle, and the minds. In a healthy democracy, *we* use them, for good. We are the saviors we've been waiting for.

That's what thousands of hands-on participants have been proving for the past ten years at EarthX, the world's largest environmental experience, held every April in Dallas, Texas.

The mission of EarthX is to end the political media war for the earth, and replace it with the biggest, widest, and deepest partnership for sustainable prosperity in the history of this planet. At EarthX, we break down the walls that divide good people inside and outside every institution, and build bridges to link them together and unleash their combined capacities. Once together, they look back and see that our institutions aren't people—they're all tools used by people to do what needs doing.

We invite everyone's worst political enemies to conspire together—as genuine human beings representing themselves, not their institutions. Because of the exceptional diversity of our participants, EarthX has been the birthplace for a surprising array of good ideas, policies, and tools to save planet earth without caving into the vested interests we're all linked to—even the ones right there in the room with us! Over 98% of our 177,326 attendees this year came to our last physical EarthX in 2019 came to learn how to live more eco-friendly lives and visit the hundreds of solution-based exhibits. But behind the scenes, at a set of conferences and meetings we call the EarthXCongress, 2,500 leaders cross every divide to come to save the world. The political media casts us as enemies, but we have learned better. At EarthX, corporate executives, environmental leaders, clean tech investors, U.S. Senators, social justice champions, and Republicans and Democrats fed up with political anger and hate all collaborate to craft potential new laws and buying practices to save oceans, forests, climate—and democracy.

We aren't the ideological warriors that battle in digital and traditional media. We are problem-solvers—"resolutionaries" from business, politics, and activism who know we're trapped by a system that profits from our war. We have chosen to end our battle and work together.

We and our partners have dedicated our lives and well over $100 million in the past ten years to learn how to shift politics from polarizing divide-and-conquer strategies to problem-solving collaborations. Lately we've found ways to break through and win.

Five years ago at EarthX, we mapped out a path to save the world's oceans, forests, and climate without sacrificing other things that make life worth living. We collaborated with democracy reformers to learn how to foster healthy political change. We've begun to implement our agenda on-the-ground in Texas and California, with reforms that breakthrough past barriers. Now we want to improve on these, broaden our base of supporters, and take these efforts national, and even global.

Our plans bring together the best ideas of conservatives and progressives, without pandering to the passions or interests of either. They would cut taxes and pollution, promote innovation and efficiency, improve health outcomes while reducing health costs, eliminate barriers to investments in clean tech, eliminate employee payroll taxes, and shift toward a circular economy with opportunities for millions left out of our consumption binge. They wouldn't trade corporatism for statism, or crony capitalism for crony socialism. They would empower people, in free and sensibly-regulated markets, to make choices that green the future.

In this book, we present many of the methods we developed at EarthXCongress—corporate executives and activist leaders at the Future

---

For additional details see https://www.congress.gov/bill/116th-congress/senate-bill/3548/text]

500 Summit, investors and entrepreneurs at the E-Capital Summit, conservatives and progressives at the BridgeUSA Summit, and each night, all of us mixing it up in banquets, dinners, and receptions where we drink, think, wheel and deal.

Most of our solutions aren't new. They just aren't politically feasible, yet. The biggest barrier to an effective green new deal is a political media system that keeps Americans from hearing, respecting, liking, and conspiring positively with each other. If we can't get past that, this war will consume us all, including the institutions that fuel it.

It is time to end the war to protect the planet, and start actually saving it instead. If you want to be part of the solution, read this book, join us at inthistogetheramerica.org and earthx.org, and join us online or in Dallas every April for EarthX. The people, ideas, and strategies are waiting for you here.

A WORD ON THE VIRUS

It could have been just another kind of flu, virulent and deadly, then gone. But in this world, at this time, the virus revealed our weaknesses. It spread faster and with more destructive consequences than if this were a healthier place.

The pandemic that changed our world appeared just as we were finishing this book. It shifted the profit center of politics and media from President Trump to COVID-19. It woke us from idol worship and demonization, and focused us on each other. It kept us apart, but reminded us we're all in this together.

Here is the bottom line: our system wasn't resilient enough to stop COVID in November 2019 from becoming the pandemic of 2020. From an ecological perspective, our whole human species now live in one giant hive. The global economic system that America launched after World War II and accelerated with the Cold War brought unprecedented material prosperity to nearly five billion of the seven billion of us. We have mastered production, built towering production machines, and turned the globe into one extensive just-in-time assembly line. We have comparative-advantaged every nation, state, and community into a part serving the whole, and the result has been magnificent, but also scary, and dangerous. We lack the boundaries and variations that restrain the spread of viruses, helpful as well as harmful. Our reward is vast material wealth, but with it, fragility. We are one enormous hormone-grown genetically-designed sitting duck. If we don't want to be plucked and carved,

XXVI   TRAMMELL S. CROW *and* BILL SHIREMAN

we need to learn a few of nature's lessons. Big is powerful, but small is beautiful. Uniformity makes things fast, but variety makes them last. We are one coextensive community, too big, too uniform, too simple, too automated, too tightly connected, too dependent on growth, too stretched, too brittle, and way too far out on a limb.

In America and the industrial world, our media has grown mechanized by algorithms that efficiently divide and divert us. Our health industry is a crony system of socialist and capitalist patronage that works miracles but costs fortunes. Our financial system is a casino, and the cards are stacked. We'd reshuffle them, but our markets are rigged, to protect the past. We'd unrig them, but our political system is corrupted. We'd vote in a new one, but our democracy is broken. We'd fix it, but it's already fixed. We'd throw out the fixers, but neither the power brokers, the managerial state, nor the intellectual elite actually control the machine. They just extract what they can, a little more or less than the rest of us, usually with neutral, good, or the best intentions. We can replace them, but we'd still be trapped. We're all in this together, living in a bubble and in danger of a burst.

The virus pierced a tiny hole in our bubble. We can patch it, but that won't hold it together long. Better to ease our way out of the bubble. Something is out there. But what?

This community of seven billion humans is nature's most astonishing reveal so far, at least in this corner of the universe. But it is not her crowning achievement, unless we make it so. She has much in store, waiting.

America is a part of the journey we're all on, a precious and exceptional part. But she has a higher nature, a better angel to aspire to. She isn't an object in a place or a time. She is an idea and an ideal. She wasn't conceived by rich white European men. She descended from the kingdoms of Africa, the philosophers of the Middle East and Asia, the political systems of the west and north, the founders here and abroad. She is not power or prosperity. She is free expression—freedom to discover and reveal everything in our nature, and the opportunity, with wisdom, to serve her well.

When in the course of human events nature sends a big message our way—a coronavirus, climate crisis, extinction pandemic, even Donald J. Trump—we are well-advised to set aside what we've been doing and listen. Something's a bit wrong. She is telling us how to make it right.

We are all an endangered political species, and we need to help each other. This is not the last challenge to our global well-being. There are many more lying in wait. The hits ahead will take us out, if we don't learn some lessons from deep in our nature, and let our next transformation begin. Her best days, and ours if we choose, are ahead.

INTRODUCTION
Climate of Denial

Three Reasons It's Time to End the War and Save the Planet Instead

You know the facts. The planet is getting hotter. Here in Texas where we're writing this, the years between 1980 and 2018 saw a record 104 weather and climate disasters.[1] And these are only the disasters that caused damages over a billion dollars. In 2011 we had our hottest summer on record.[2] That triggered the Texas Drought that was finally interrupted May 2015—when it gave way to a stormy deluge of biblical proportions, giving us the wettest month in our history. Then the wettest year[3] washed away $8.7 billion in agricultural value.[4] Cities along our gulf bore the brunt. Port Isabel experienced 121 days of coastal flooding from 2005 to 2015—eight times the rate in the decade starting in 1955.[5]

That's just in the American southwest. Globally, temperatures have risen 1.4°F in a century, with two-thirds of the rise since 1975.[6] The assault

1 NOAA National Centers for Environmental Information (NCEI). 2019. "Billion-Dollar Weather and Climate Disasters: Table of Events." Accessed October 24, 2019. https://www.ncdc.noaa.gov/billions/events/TX/1980-2019.

2 NOAA NCEI. 2019. "State Climate Summaries: Texas." Accessed October 24, 2019. https://state-summaries.ncics.org/chapter/tx/.

3 National Weather Service. 2019. "DFW—Monthly and Annual Precipitation." Accessed October 24, 2019. https://www.weather.gov/fwd/dmoprecip.

4 Bolhassani, Behni. 2014. "The 2011 Texas Drought: Its Impact and Implications." Texas Water Policy, November 24, 2014. http://www.texaswaterpolicy.com/blog/2015/1/23/the-2011-texas-drought-its-impacts-and-implications.

5 The Climate Reality Project. 2016. "What Does Climate Change Mean for Texas?" Accessed October 24, 2019. https://www.climaterealityproject.org/blog/what-does-climate-change-mean-texas.

6 NASA Earth Observatory. 2019. "World of Change: Global Temperatures." Accessed October 24, 2019. https://earthobservatory.nasa.gov/world-of-change/DecadalTemp.

on the planet is nothing less than a war, our friend Bill McKibben tells us. "We're under attack from climate change ... With each passing week, another 22,000 square miles of Arctic ice disappears. In the Pacific ... the enemy (is) waging a full-scale assault on the region's coral reefs (reducing) the Great Barrier Reef ... to white bone-yards." And "millions of refugees are fleeing the horrors of war, their numbers swelling daily as they're forced to abandon their homes to escape famine and desolation and disease."[7]

This wholesale assault on climate stability is now triggering a series of ecological disasters. The first system to fail appears to be the world's tropical reefs, the source of most of the ocean's ecological diversity and productivity. Soon, if we don't act, sea-level rise will flood the Persian Gulf, Polynesia, and one after another, most of the world's coastal cities. Europe will be claimed by permanent drought; and vast areas of China, India, and Bangladesh by desert. The end of human civilization is a very real possibility.

In the face of this mortal threat, many of our friends say the next step is clear:

"Declare war on climate change," naturalist Bill McKibben tells us. "Our only hope is to mobilize like we did in WWII."

If ever any war were justified, it would be to save the planet. But is war the answer? Where do we enlist? And who should we fight?

Clearly, Americans have a fondness for war. We are revolutionaries. Our nation was born in a war for independence, consecrated in a bloody civil war to end slavery, and superpowered when we annihilated fascism in the Second World War, quite possibly saving western civilization and liberal democracy in the process.

War is, politicians often say, our "last resort," yet we seem to reach for it first. No problem is truly deemed worthy of our focus until we've declared war on it. The War on Poverty, War on Cancer, War on Drugs, War on Terror, War on Hunger, and now War on Climate Change have all been declared to help us sort through various competing challenges and choose which to mobilize against. None of these wars have been won, however most drag on for decades. Many make matters worse.

---

7 McKibbon, Bill. 2016. "A World at War." The New Republic, August 15, 2016. https://newrepublic. com/article/135684/declare-war-climate-change-mobilize-wwii.

The success rate is not much better for the hotter and deadlier wars we have waged during our lifetimes in Cuba, Thailand, the Dominican Republic, Bolivia, Vietnam, Cambodia, Zaire, Lebanon, Grenada, Nicaragua, El Salvador, Libya, Iraq (twice), Afghanistan, or Syria. Each simply drags on, without end, through interludes of comparatively restrained killing.

Except for Grenada. We clearly liberated Grenada.

We lose nearly all these wars because fighting can't win what we now seek. The War on Climate Change is no different. It is not a new war. This is just the latest surge. Since the Santa Barbara oil spill led to the first Earth Day in 1970,[8] we and other environmentalists waged war against giant corporations—especially big oil—to help save the earth. The two of us joined protests, circulated petitions, organized citizens, debated energy executives, and eventually ran campaigns, losing some and winning some.

The early battles helped generate a decade of major successes, most in the 1970s: the Clean Air Act, Clean Water Act, National Environmental Policy Act, the U.S. Environmental Protection Agency, and more.

But over the past 40 years, we've outsourced the climate war to entrenched institutions that profit more by perpetuating than ending it. We're not talking just about the adversaries themselves—big oil, chemical, agricultural, and industrial giants on one side, and environmental activists, clean tech investors, lawyers, organizers, and communicators on the other. The biggest beneficiaries in the war for the earth are the media and political industries.

This book makes a simple proposition: **Declare an end to the war to save the planet.** Then collaborate to save it.

We're not talking surrender. The job we started hasn't been finished. Conflicts will continue. Much legitimately divides us. But the time for outright war is over. There's work to do.

There are at least three reasons the war for the planet is now the enemy of the planet. First, the war drives denial—and not just climate denial.

---

8 Thulin, Lila. 2019. "How an Oil Spill 50 Years Ago Inspired the First Earth Day." Accessed October 24, 2019. https://www.smithsonianmag.com/history/how-oil-spill-50-years-ago-inspired-first-earth-day-180972007/.

Relentless gloom-and-doom triggers urgency, alarm, and eventually exhaustion. We can't live without hope for long. Apathy and denial are thick shields against despair.

Second, the war builds more opposition than support. It raises armies on both sides. Environmentalists see their budgets grow and think they're making progress. But those we attack build fortresses against us. They institutionalize the conflict. Build it into their plans. Retain political and media strategists to manage it endlessly. Grow comfortable with our enmity. Once that happens, collaboration becomes a threat to both sides—the war is a profit center too lucrative to end.

For example, in 2016 when naturalist Bill McKibben declared war on climate change in The New Republic, 29 foundations soon committed $4 billion in grants to climate change.[9,10] Starting in election year 2020, Republican strategists declared a political emergency. The left was launching an attack on capitalism, they warned us and a dozen top-tier donors. It's time to step up and match that $4 billion, dollar-for-dollar, the strategists insisted.

We might wonder what they were smoking, but there's more than a whiff of truth in it. To separate conservative donors from their money, GOP fundraisers gleefully quote progressives when they blame capitalism for all our challenges and declare climate change as a vehicle for advancing a progressive big government agenda.

That leads to the third reason to move beyond war as our first resort: to the media and political strategists, Planet Earth is now more valuable dying than living—so long as the final end happens after the next election.

We first came to understand this during the Obama administration, when White House Chief of Staff Rahm Emanuel made the decision not to press hard for Senate approval of a cap-and-trade climate bill in 2009. The political costs—including the possible loss of Democratic House and Senate—were too great.

9 McKibbon, Bill. 2016. "A World at War." The New Republic, August 15, 2016. https://newrepublic. com/article/135684/declare-war-climate-change-mobilize-wwii.
10 Hewlett Foundation. 2018. "Philanthropic Community Announces $4 Billion Commitment to Combat Climate Change." Press Release, September 14, 2018. https://hewlett.org/newsroom/philan-thropic-community-announces-4-billion-commitment-to-combat-climate-change/.

Two years after, we saw the scenario play out in even starker form on the Republican side of the aisle when the CEO of one of the largest electric utilities reported on his meeting with a powerful Republican Senator. He told the Senator that his company could accept the Clean Power Plan proposed by President Obama. The Senator thanked him for his input. Then a top party fundraiser and strategist sat down with him in another room, and explained political reality to the CEO. As he paraphrased it, the conversation went like this: *We've spent millions turning climate into a wedge issue. We rely on it to keep our base united against Democrats. We need that to keep our majority. So regardless of your opinion, we need you to stick to the party line: "Stop the job-killing EPA." If you can't, we may not be able to protect your top tax and regulatory priorities.*

Let us say that again. A top energy CEO says his company can accept EPA climate regulations. But the battle against those regulations is too valuable to the *political* industry to resolve.

We've now heard parallel stories from a half-dozen other executives. Most are surprised that we are surprised. To many in the political industry, this is how business is done, impure and simple.

It's not just Republican denial that stops climate action—it's Democratic denial too. Both agree we face a crisis. What divides us is that we have competing nightmare scenarios.

The left is most frightened by ecological catastrophe. To avert the disastrous consequences that loom ahead, liberals propose what liberals always seem to propose: a massive intervention by government, to impose rules and taxes on corporations, to shift power back to "people"—mostly via "democratic" institutions that can compel a rapid conversion to 100% carbon-free clean energy.

The right is most frightened by economic catastrophe. To avert the disastrous consequences that loom ahead, conservatives propose what conservatives always seem to propose: a massive reduction in government, with tax and regulatory cuts that shift power back to "people"—mostly via corporations that can deliver what we need at a lower cost without the burdens of big government.

Die-hard conservatives absolutely refuse to take climate change seriously. It's not so much that they deny the science. They just hate the proposed solutions. Their easiest rebuttal is to publicly proclaim the whole issue a hoax, while they privately acknowledge it's real, but preferable to the loss of freedoms required if we act.

Die-hard liberals absolutely refuse to take fiscal limits seriously. It's not so much that they deny the limits. They just hate the proposed solutions: cutting taxes on corporations and the wealthy, and abandoning Social Security and Medicare. Their easiest rebuttal is to publicly proclaim the whole fiscal limits issue a hoax, while they privately acknowledge that deficits are preferable to the loss of social protections if we act.

Why do liberals deny economic limits, while conservatives deny ecological ones? More to the point, why do both Democratic and Republican politicians drive us toward both economic and ecological bankruptcy when either is in power?

They ignore those limits because the vested interests that pay their bills make more money by perpetuating the climate war than by resolving it.

So long as the right and left cling to their denials—one of economic and the other of ecological limits—we will solve neither. The status quo interest groups who choreograph the war will keep their power, as the nation and world march toward both economic and ecological catastrophe.

If we look more closely at our economic and ecological crises, we find them connected at the root. They both result from a system that drives non-sustainable growth and mounting debt. The growth takes money from people and resources from the environment. It leaves the people with massive debt and the environment with colossal damage. The money helps prop up big old institutions that are way overdue for creative disruption. Big corporations and big government both "benefit" in the short term from this system. Their managers know how to exploit it for gain. But the protection they receive sets them up for failure in due course. If our economic and ecological foundations collapse, they will perish along with the rest of us. They too need to change. Their leaders know it. But none of them can act until the public compels them to, together.

The key is to build a left-to-right alliance for solutions that combine the best ideas of both conservatives *and* progressives while pandering to the vested interests of neither.

To save our environment, we also have to save our economy and our democracy. That's the politically incorrect strategy we propose in this book. It's a strategy that can work.

It is time for a grand coalition between the grassroots and grasstops left and right, to gently but firmly challenge the tired status quo institutions that drive up both forms of debt, and resolve our fiscal and environmental challenges simultaneously.

It won't be easy to forge an authentic right-left coalition to protect the environment. But we have an advantage: the same kinds of policies that can save the planet can also save the economy and the middle class, and even contribute to a less divided American democracy.

To understand how progressives and conservatives can work together, however, we need to understand how we're different, how we fit together, and how a left-right coalition can make our nation whole.

PART ONE: THE PEOPLE

Who is In This Together?

CHAPTER ONE
THE STORY

TRAMMELL'S STORY

In 1961, when I was six, I asked my father, "Daddy, daddy, are we Democrat or are we Republican?" "Neither, son," he boomed back to me. "We're conservative."

My dad never waved a flag of any kind, but he was a Republican because he followed three credos that I took to, after some experimentation, as my own: social moderation, fiscal conservation, and service to country.

It was the 1960s, the Vietnam War was raging, the civil rights movement was growing, and I didn't know if we should be communists, socialists, or capitalists. When my older brother Harlan returned home from military school at Thanksgiving in 1966, it was this archetypal homecoming of the heroic big brother. Harlan took me aside and taught me three words: politics, environment, and population. And it just took. I knew from then that those three would be the drivers of my life. Saving the environment was the purpose I would serve. Overpopulation was the problem I would help overcome. And politics was essential to the solution I could help bring.

In college, when Richard Nixon was President, I defied my dad and campaigned for George McGovern in the black ghettos of New Haven, thinking he and his socially democratic policies would be the best for people and the environment. But when my father made me cut my hair and major in economics, it didn't take me long to realize that free enter-prise—call it capitalism, just don't call it crony capitalism—can deliver what social democrats can only promise. Capitalism drives what John F. Kennedy called a rising tide that lifts all boats. That has been my political conviction ever since, and most of my classmates at Yale and colleagues in Dallas and across the country live by it.

It's a mystery to me why that word environment became the most important in the world to me at age 12, and remained so, mostly latent, for decades. I didn't immediately make it a major focus of my life. I joined the family business, got married, and had children. Along the way, I kicked off a Dallas recycling program and built some green buildings, not realizing that however small these steps were, in the city of Dallas, they amounted to a significant signal to local politicians to take up the cause.

When I was 43 years old, my marriage ended. In the confusion of it all, I forgot to go back to work and found myself retired by mistake at an early age. I focused on my kids, and spent my spare time chairing the city's recycling task force, helping grow a green building council, and contributing to a handful of environmental campaigns. In Austin, the state capital, I helped start Texas Campaign for the Environment, and in Washington, D.C., Republicans for Environmental Protection. But my efforts were part-time at most.

I finally got out of my environmental easy-chair about 10 years ago, when two businessmen, Garrett Boone, and David Litman—the founders of The Container Store and hotels.com respectively—came to me and told me, "You're the only Texas Republican businessman we can find who's interested in the environment." They asked me to join them in a campaign to stop TXU, our local utility, from building eleven new coal-fired plants they were trying to fast-track with Governor Rick Perry.

That immediately sent up red flags to me. It was common knowledge that we didn't need any new coal plants—certainly not eleven of them. TXU was playing the state for a larger capital base to justify higher revenues at the expense of ratepayers and air breathers.

To stop them, we created Texas Business for Clean Air—the first time there has ever been an organization with "business" and "clean" together in Texas.[11] As the Paul Revere of the group, the recruiting officer, I got on the horn every day, until late into the night, recruiting business leaders in Dallas, Fort Worth, Houston, Austin, San Antonio, and El Paso until my fist seemed permanently affixed to my ear. But I was enlightened that so many business leaders would fight the system, the establishment. Because the utility companies are members of every country club, every chamber of commerce, and every civic committee in the state. For business leaders to go up against them was surprising and inspiring to me.

Garrett, David, and I found that with 250 business leaders behind us, doors were open to us anywhere in the Texas Capitol that we wanted to go. As business leaders, we changed the minds of many of our very conservative state lawmakers. Our group was just one of many, but we created the imprimatur of business support politicians needed to change course. After two years, TXU was acquired by Goldman-Sachs, KKR, and Texas Pacific Group, and negotiated with environmentalists to shift the company away from coal dependence and toward renewables.[12] We had won.

The TXU fight woke me up and converted me into a full-time pro-business environmentalist. Having that realization—that business leaders would step up if we asked them to—I knew that business could play an essential role in a solution. I didn't carefully research my next steps. I just dove in. I decided Texas needed a good old-fashioned Earth Day celebration, where business leaders and environmentalists could come together for an exposition, so Texans with little awareness of what the problems are and solutions could quickly climb a very steep learning curve.

We called it Earth Day Dallas. Our first year in 2011, I put together a ragtag team of friends, and we got on the horn and started inviting people. Together we lined up 200 exhibitors and 38,000 people, and that first year discovered we were the largest environmental expo in the

11 Texas Business For Clean Air PAC. 2009. "History Of Texas Business for Clean Air PAC." Accessed October 24, 2019. http://www.txbca.org/about.html.
12 NRDC. 2007. "Record TXU Buyout Includes Unprecedented Global Warming, Emissions Plan." NRDC Press Release, February 26, 2007. https://www.nrdc.org/media/2007/070226.

country. Everyone was a part of it—Republicans and Democrats, animal eaters and animal protectors, God-fearing Christians and goddess-revering New Agers, salespeople for cars and salespeople for causes.

It turns out that almost everyone supports clean air, clean water, and healthy ecosystems. How could we not? We love our children more than anything, and without a planet to live on, their future is highly constrained. Since we're a democracy, and we all agree, saving the planet should be pretty easy, right?

Almost, but not quite. Even in a democracy, we can't just ask for what we want or even vote for it. We need to get involved, we are reminded. Democracy has a price, and we need to pay our dues.

So I entered the political world. I knew freedom wasn't free, but I'd never seen the price list until I got involved in electoral politics. Meeting a politician, securing a vote, getting legislation introduced, scheduling a hearing, moving an important policy change to the floor, having it heard—it turns out there's a price for each of these steps, and the myriad others required to change a law. And that's just the start.

Nonetheless, I dove in, teaming up with friends to write checks to politicians, bundlers, PACs, SuperPACs, and dozens of "non-political" voter education organizations raising public awareness about issues I cared about. I was confident that if we just outspent the friends writing checks to stop the laws we wanted, we'd win.

People like me have now spent billions of dollars on campaigns to protect the climate. In the next four years, at least $5 billion more has already been pledged, in addition to the official campaign contributions, to make sure climate is a major issue in the 2020 presidential election ahead. The dollars to be traded are immense in number—but the sacrifice will be worth it, if we get to save our planet.

But here's the problem: the dollars we spend, ostensibly to save the planet and promote social justice, will trigger almost as many dollars on the other side, not to destroy the planet, but ostensibly to save the economy and promote freedom. Our campaign will be transformed by the media and political industry into an attack on prosperity and liberty. And it won't be just fake news: the proposals that make political headway will be those that pit the environment against the economy, and justice against freedom. They won't be the sensible solutions that almost everyone supports. They'll be ideological non-solutions that keep the left and right at war.

Here's why. I know you don't want to believe it, but this is the truth. It's not the climate deniers who are blocking us. It's not Big Oil, Big Gas, or even Small-and-Getting-Smaller Coal. Yes, they often oppose us, but they're not the adversaries who beat us. The political industry is what's beating us—the industry dependent on our money, and the money of our adversaries, to keep this battle going, for as long as we all keep paying them to fight it.

That's when I began to learn a difficult truth. Politics isn't just the solution to the problem. Politics is also the problem.

BILL'S STORY

I became an environmental activist when I was eight, when my favorite person in the world died. The sudden loss of my grandfather sent the reality of mortality crashing down upon me, and left me quite literally on the floor, crying quietly without my parents noticing, at both my cataclysmic personal loss and my stunning realization. My family was not a religious one, so the idea of God in heaven to me sounded as unlikely as Santa Claus at the North Pole, and a lot more consequential. It meant that my grandfather had perished more absolutely than I could bear—and that everyone else I loved would too. With no illusory savior to offer me everlasting life, mortality became a powerful motivator to me.

It was the mid-1960s. The anti-war and civil rights movements were raging, the "throwaway society" seemed to be burying us in pollution and waste, and women (along with many men) were waking up to the realization that something was missing from their lives, a deficit of personal meaning and power imposed gently but firmly by a system that treated them not as distinctive individuals with agency, but as generic and relatively purposeless "consumers" who came in four basic varieties: male, female, white, and not white.

With a social awakening happening all around me, I wanted to be a part of meeting those challenges. I had heard that pollution, overpopulation, and the prospect of nuclear war were real threats not just to me, but to all life on earth. With my grandfather's memory as my driver, I decided I'd better take action.

Although I was introverted and self-conscious, I had channeled my quiet disquiet in ways that gave me a sense of personal power. I started a candy and soda shop that catered to kids from four nearby schools, who hung out in our atrium loading up on simple carbs for the ten years that took them from childhood to adolescence. I grew up with them, and as I fed them with sugar, I became increasingly concerned about issues like war, justice, the environment, and health. To be a socially responsible entrepreneur, I pushed fruits and nutrition bars too—with limited success—and charged deposits on soda cans so the kids would return them for a refund. That way I could recycle them at our high school ecology center.

But I knew that wasn't enough. So in junior high, I started a little political campaign button company that made money and simultaneously helped pro-environment candidates I liked raise funds and get their message out. Liberty Badge Company wasn't quite the money machine of other Silicon Valley startups, but it did pay most of my way through college, where I registered Republican and joined up with consumer advocate Ralph Nader to promote a California "bottle bill" so consumers would return ten billion empty cans and bottles a year for recycling.

We were young and idealistic and figured that with Nader on our side, politicians would bend to the will of the people, and pass our recycling bill into law. So when the state's politicians blocked it from even reaching the State Senate floor, we went directly to the people, organizing volunteers to collect a half-million signatures to place the bottle bill on the state ballot. Alas, beer and soda companies spent $5 million to bury that effort, and in 1982 the voters turned us down.

Broke and exhausted, my colleagues decided to toss leadership of our campaign to 24-year-old me. I applied the skills I had learned from Nader to take the battle back to Sacramento—where we were soundly defeated. But I had another strategy in mind, one I had learned not from the political left, but from my friends on the right: I decided to talk to conservatives.

I reached out to two of my "enemies"—a major brewer named Bill Coors and a religious conservative retail executive named Chuck Collings. They courageously stepped ahead of their competitors and joined forces with environmentalists to solve the problem. Together we recruited a Democratic Assemblyman named Burt Margolin and a Republican State Senator named Becky Morgan to introduce an innovative new California deposit law. With backing from business, labor, and environmentalists, politicians from both parties—with some substantial coaxing—were happy to pass the bill and get that issue off their desks for good.

Our recycling law worked, much better than my ideological critics on both the right and left had predicted. It borrowed ideas from the left to increase its effectiveness and ideas from the right that kept costs down. The experience was in some ways traumatic—politics is a vicious game— but also triumphant, and so validating that I decided to do it some more. In the decade that followed, I built similar coalitions of business, activists, conservatives, and progressives, to help protect forests, oceans, and the global climate.

If my grandfather only knew.

Over the years I've discovered a more credible religious sensibility, hinted to me during long excursions deep into nature. I have grown to appreciate higher causes other than protecting the environment, like freedom, justice, and reverence for a power greater than us. I sense now how all these and we are in some way one.

So when I met my fellow traveler and source of unrelenting energy, Trammell S. Crow, I was ready.

TRAMMELL AND BILL

We met in 2013 when Bill journeyed to Dallas, Texas, in search of the endangered Republican environmentalist once feared extinct but hiding in the closet to escape discovery. Trammell had helped stop a multibillion-dollar crony capitalist boondoggle to impose coal plants on Texas ratepayers. He won, but knew that wasn't enough. So, in order to educate and motivate citizens to take the steps to come, he went on to build the largest Earth Day exposition in the world—not in New York, Seattle, or San Francisco, but right there in Dallas.

Trammell put Bill in the driver's seat of his Tesla, badgering him to drive it faster and faster, to a local barbecue. There, for two hours, they shared their frustrations about a political system that had torn the nation into warring tribes of Republican climate deniers and Democratic climate catastrophists, each believing the other to be diabolical and in need of political annihilation. Bill offered to bring the adversaries right there to Trammell's Earth Day event, where he said that corporate executives, passionate activists, conservative Republicans, and progressive Democrats—plus libertarians and other orphans of the two-party duopoly—could discover they were co-catalysts of the most positive and powerful kind.

The EarthxFuture500 Summit, now a fixture at EarthX, became our forum to fashion together solutions to ecological challenges that don't fit the prescribed left-versus-right narrative, and that are friendly to freedom, justice, and authentic prosperity all at once.[13]

That summit triggered more. We invited investors, donors, politicians, and issue advocates to come to Earth Day Texas, and bring their own communities. And they came.

---

13 EarthX. 2019. "EarthxFuture500 Summit." Accessed October 24, 2019. https://earthx.org/conference/earthxfuture500summit/.

TRAMMELL AND THE EARTHX CELEBRATION

Today, rebranded EarthX, we annually convene 12 conferences, 400 speakers, 2,500 national and global leaders, 750 exhibitors, and about 175,000 of our closest friends to explore how we can save the planet together. With 30 full-length documentary films and 100 virtual reality experiences to guide us, you could call our little get-together a Texas melee.

We traded "Day" for "X" in our name because everyone crosses our path. Those 175,000 people make EarthX the largest Earth Day exposition in the world—in fact, the largest single-weekend environmental exhibition period.

How do we attract so many to Dallas for a tree-hugging event? Blood, sweat, money, and tears play a part. But the biggest reason is that we are meeting an unmet need, and tapping an audience that progressive coastal environmentalists miss: conservative Middle America loves the earth too. We just have different ways of showing it.

We also reach out and invite leaders—about 2,500 hand-picked corporate executives, environmental donors, clean tech investors, grass-roots activists, student leaders, scientific experts, and political leaders from both parties. We don't gather them just to talk—though we admit there's an awful lot of that. We invite them for action—to take action, trigger action, and reward action.

We assemble corporate executives, donors, and activists together for the EarthX Future 500 Summit, to drive corporate-NGO partnerships to save oceans, forests, and climate.

We invite mainstream and social investors to fund innovators and entrepreneurs at the EarthX E-Capital Summit.

We gather conservatives, progressives, college students, and politicians to drive bipartisan policy solutions at the EarthX Bridge Summit.

We hold banquets, host receptions, and provide meeting space for dozens of change agents across all these communities so they can engage with each other and share ideas.

And quite a number of us gather at my home in the evenings, for the all-important afterparties where some of the juiciest conspiracies are hatched.

These gatherings put our ecological challenges right on the table. There is to be no greenwashing at EarthX, but also no blacklisting. We learn of the threats, the losses, and the failures. We name the companies, NGOs, and politicians whose support and action we need. But we also see the progress, the commitments, and the determination to succeed. And we build diverse communities with all the people and ideas needed to make a difference.

We see "enemies" working together. Oil executives sitting down with Greenpeace activists and finding common ground. Food and agriculture executives forging partnerships with rainforest champions. It's surprising, and inspiring, to see what can come of a chance meeting—or an arranged coincidence—at EarthX.

The atmosphere at EarthX is one of optimism. It's more than hope. It's anticipation. We expect to succeed. With our eyes and our minds open to diverse people and ideas, we will save the planet.

Our experiences at EarthX convince us that there is a better way to save Mother Earth than political warfare. War is not the answer here. Battles are necessary, and we know they will continue. But the environmental movement is not about battling the old. It is about evolving into something new. A new culture that transcends and includes what came before. A culture where we wake up in the morning and realize we aren't just consumers in a produce-and-consume economy—we are creators on a planet, a living, breathing world that sustains us as we sustain her.

CHAPTER TWO
THE PROTECTORS
AND THE LIBERATORS

HOW THE LEFT AND RIGHT FIT TOGETHER

One of us lives in Dallas, where it's practically impossible to be an out-of-the-closet progressive. The other lives in San Francisco, where it's legal to be almost anything but a conservative.

Or so it seems. But the reality is different. San Franciscans can be extraordinarily conservative, especially in preserving the power of vested interests that show off their progressive stripes while exploiting the left to keep their regressive power. And in Dallas, we lean culturally to the right and protect our fossil fuel traditions, but we've also reformed our electric utilities and grown the nation's most robust clean energy industry.

Scratch the surface in any community, and you will find that even if they don't call themselves conservatives and progressives, champions of both are contending with one another. It's a part of our nature.

The truth is, no matter where we come from or where we go, about half of us lean politically to the right, and half of us to the left. There's a reason for that.

It's hard for partisans to accept—we've been taught to hate each other so. But conservatives and progressives are made for each other. When we are kept apart, we fight. When we're brought together, we fit.

The left and right don't just see the world from different perspectives. We see different worlds. The liberal worldview, as set forth by the great 18th century French political theorist Jean-Jacques Rousseau, tells us that people are naturally selfless, and that nature is supportive of our needs.[14] The conservative worldview, as 17th century English political philosopher Thomas Hobbes famously explained, is the opposite: people are naturally selfish, and nature is threatening.[15]

The truth is that conservatives and liberals are each half-right: people are both selfless and selfish, and nature is both supportive and threatening. Liberals and conservatives reflect these two realities, but each specializes in a different aspect of it. That is why in this book we call conservatives the Protectors, and liberals the Liberators.

The Protectors on our political right, seeing that people are selfish and nature threatening, are always alert to the dangers that lurk inside and outside our communities. The Liberators on our political left, seeing that people are selfless and nature is supportive, are always looking to free us from the limits of oppressive forces that keep us from attaining our potential. These two communities of complementary opposites are often at odds and frequently engage in political warfare. But by vying together in conflict, they help keep our nation both safe and free.

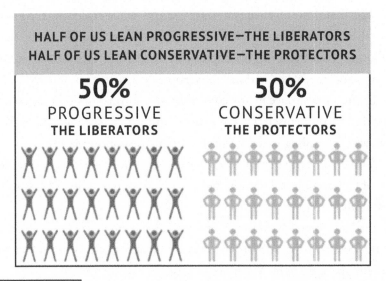

HALF OF US LEAN PROGRESSIVE–THE LIBERATORS
HALF OF US LEAN CONSERVATIVE–THE PROTECTORS

50%
PROGRESSIVE
THE LIBERATORS

50%
CONSERVATIVE
THE PROTECTORS

---

14 Rousseau, Jean-Jacques. 2018. *Rousseau: The Social Contract and Other Later Political Writings.* Second edition. Edited by Victor Gourevitch. United Kingdom: Cambridge University Press.
15 Finn, Stephen. 2019. "Thomas Hobbes: Methodology." *Internet Encyclopedia of Philosophy.* https://www.iep.utm.edu/hobmeth/.

But today, America seems divided like never before. Not even after the Civil War did Americans feel such bitter ideological separation from one another. Not since the Vietnam War has fraternization between the political left and right been so discouraged.

Yet the reality is that 70% of us can agree on solutions that resolve even the toughest issues that divide us—even the four wedge issues: abortion, guns, immigration, and climate.

It's not that 7 in 10 always agree when polled—but they learn to agree, as they engage with one another. That's not always obvious when we rely mostly on opinion polls to learn the political views of other groups.[16] The news media looks to respected bipartisan pollsters like Pew Research Center[17] and Gallup, Inc.[18] Political scientists and other scholars look to more academic sources like the General Social Survey[19] and the National Election Studies.[20] Partisan strategies mostly retain private pollsters who work almost exclusively for just one party, such as Peter Hart for Democrats and Frank Luntz for Republicans. To the general public, polls tell us what people believe. But to professionals who analyze them, they also teach how to change what people believe, or more often, manipulate our behavior based on what we believe.[21]

We use polls to inform our work, but they don't tell us the whole story of who people are or how we fit together. Far from it. They measure us simplistically and non-dynamically. They identify our worries and fears, and provide clear evidence of how to transform fear into hate, and direct

16 Geer, John Gray. 2004. Public Opinion and Polling Around the World: A Historical Encyclopedia. Volume 1. Santa Barbara, CA: ABC-CLIO.
17 Pew Research Center. 2019. "About Pew Research Center." Accessed November 19, 2019. https://www.pewresearch.org/about/.
18 Gallup. 2019. "Gallup Poll." Accessed November 19, 2019. https://news.gallup.com/poll/101905/gallup-poll.aspx.
19 NORC at the University of Chicago. 2019. "General Social Survey (GSS)." Accessed November 19, 2019. http://www.norc.org/Research/Projects/Pages/general-social-survey.aspx.
20 ANES (American National Election Studies). 2019. "About Us." Accessed November 19, 2019. https://electionstudies.org/about-us/.
21 For additional discussion on polarization see:
Carmines, Edward G., Michael J. Ensley, and Michael W. Wagner. 2012. "Who Fits the Left–Right Divide? Partisan Polarization in the American Electorate". American Behavioral Scientist 56 (12): 1631–1653. Claassen, Ryan L. and Benjamin Highton. 2008. "Policy Polarization among Party Elites and the Significance of Political Awareness in the Mass Public". Political Research Quarterly. 62 (3): 538–551. Fiorina, Morris, P., and Samuel J. Abrams. 2008. "Political Polarization in the American Public." Annual Review of Political Science 11 (1): 563-588. Layman, Geoffrey C., Thomas M Carsey, and Juliana Menasce Horowitz. 2006. "Party Polarization in American Politics: Characteristics, Causes, and Consequences." Annual Review of Political Science 9 (1): 83–110.

it toward groups that someone wants us to despise. But they don't tell us how to see the best in others or have hope in the midst of complex change.

Our approach is different. You can learn more about our methods in books like Engaging Outraged Stakeholders.[22] But bottom line, we engage people who have often been taught to fear and hate each other —conservatives, progressives, capitalists, and activists. Because each sees others as demons, our first step is to humanize all sides, by engaging them in informal processes of relationship-building. This undermines the demonization and opens the door to understanding and partnership.

Once a human relationship is established, we engage the individuals in discussions about issues that divide them. We help them dig deeper than the surface issues that the media exploits. We have them explore the roots of the dispute, at least five levels down. This moves them past their disputes, and into territory where common ground is likely. Finally, we look to science, nature, markets and other complex systems that lead us to root-cause solutions.

POLLS, DATA, AND EXPERIENCE: WHAT WE LEARN FROM EACH

This book describes half of us as conservative Protectors who lean right, and half as progressive Liberators who lean left. Each half includes a contingent of about 15 percent we call Warriors, and around 35% on each side who are Civilians, including potential Solution Citizens. Combining the Civilians on the left and right, we find (and other researchers agree) that an "exhausted majority" of about 70% are effectively disenfranchised in the current system.

The numbers and proportions vary by time, place, and especially definition. It's rarely true that we split exactly half left and half right, or that 7 in 10 of us can work things out, while 3 in 10 can't. Those three sets of numbers come from a combination of three sources: polls, data, and experience. What validates them is not their source, but their effectiveness. In practice, they lead us to

---

22 Shireman, Bill, Erik Wohlgemuth, and Danna Pfahl. 2013. Engaging Outraged Stakeholders: How-To Guide for Uniting the Left, Right, Capitalists, and Activists. New York, NY: Affinity Press.

solutions that a decisive majority can support and a critical mass of influencers will commit to. They work.

Polls point us in the right direction, but aren't enough by themselves.   Across party lines, for example, a little over 70% say the government is spending too little on education, and that illegal drugs are a serious issue in the U.S. More than 80% favor concerted government action to protect the environment. Fox News reports that 65% of registered voters say climate change is a major problem that the government should address. The Associated Press reports that roughly three out of four people believe climate change is happening. Reuters/Ipsos finds that almost 70% of Americans want the U.S. to take aggressive action to combat climate change.

Compare survey results by the American National Election Studies, Fox News, Gallup, Kaiser Family Foundation, NORC at the University of Chicago, and the Pew Research Center, and you will find a range of results, one to fit a range of expectations. Politicians can pick and choose, revealing favorable polls to the public while studying unfavorable ones privately to guide their steps.

Party identification should be straightforward to measure – after all, people register their choice with the government.   But most polls assign partisanship by asking individuals which party they identify with or lean toward. Gallup says 26% of us consider ourselves liberal/progressive, 35% conservative, and the rest moderate or reluctant to state.   Pew finds that 38% identify as politically independent, but most lean toward one of the two major parties – often to avoid the stench of the other. Fox News reports that 46% of people identify or lean Democrat while 43% identify or lean Republican. Only 12 identify independent.   The extreme left and right also don't poll precisely 15% each. ANES finds 21% identify as a strong democrat and 16% strong republican while Fox News reports 12% identify as very liberal, and 14% very conservative.

Data analysis is the second tool that helps inform our findings. **Research for More in Common's** Hidden Tribes project found that Americans believe we are far more divided than we actually are. They estimate that 55% of Republicans and Democrats hold at least one extreme view on a major issue. But in specific cases like immigration, racism, and law enforcement, the actual proportion of extremists is half the number most citizens expect. This perception gap is in part a result of the power of conflict to attract attention, win votes, and sell ads. But even conflict can't hold our attention forever. Hidden Tribes finds that an "exhausted majority" of 67% opt-out of the political warfare. This supermajority of what they call traditional liberals, passive liberals, politically disengaged, and traditional conservatives are open-minded and willing to hear others.

Experience, however, is the most powerful validator. It also makes an important point: the precise numbers only matter if you're trying to eke out an electoral victory by driving a specific voter segment to the polls. If you're trying to resolve a conflict and solve a problem, all you need to know is this: get a typical group of people together in a well-facilitated process, and while a vocal minority might rage, a significant majority will find a solution they can all agree on.

Scholars argue that most people have an exaggerated faith in their understanding of complex issues. Asking others to explain their ideas in depth, in a discussion rather than a debate, helps them moderate their own views, and integrate them with other perspectives.[23]

In a quarter-century of experience at the non-profit Future 500, we have found that no matter the issue, around 7 of 10 disparate partisans consistently find solutions to the problems that divide them when they are part of a skillfully-facilitated process of engagement. Even on hot-button wedge issues like abortion, guns, immigration, and climate, 3 in 10 or fewer remain doggedly committed to an absolute once they hear and understand an alternative point of view.

23 Abramowitz, Alan, and Saunders, Kyle L. 2005. "Why Can't We All Just Get Along? The Reality of Polarized America." The Forum 3 (2): 1–22.
Fernbach, Phillip, Todd Rogers, Craig Fox, Steven Sloman. 2013. "Political Extremism Is Supported by an Illusion of Understanding." Psychological Science, 24 (6): 939–946.

Given this human capacity to solve problems together even in tough situations, if ours were a healthy democracy, we would have effectively settled issues like climate protection decades ago.

So why don't we get together and agree? What is keeping these 70% of Americans apart?

Today's media and political industries profit by avoiding genuine discussion across partisan lines. Instead, they keep us separate, on different channels, where they can play us off against each other, by triggering our primal fear that those "other" people pose great danger to our existence.

In the age of "big data," provoking conflict is not just an unsavory art these days—it is an increasingly precise science. Political and media strategists have 24/7 access to powerful databases with vast amounts of personal information on each of us. Platforms like Catalist on the left and DataTrust on the right each contain more than 300 data points on each of America's 240 million eligible voters. At any moment, they can develop, test, and correlate messages designed to unhinge us. They can look up where we live, who we know, what we buy, where we go, causes we care about, candidates we support, schools we attend, sports we play, and the habits, obsessions, and addictions that may drive us, in awesome and disturbing detail. With this data, they are able to model our behavior and predict the effects of trigger messages with surprising accuracy. Cognitive scientists, pollsters, and analysts tap vast pools of data to trigger our fears and direct them toward whatever enemies serve their interests[24]

The cause is simple: the division of America between red and blue is driven by an entrenched set of interest groups that profit from our division. Don't get us wrong: there is no single orchestrated conspiracy at work here. No one is in charge. That's what makes it so hard to find a

---

24 For more discussion see:

Campbell, David E., John C. Green, and Geoffrey C. Layman. 2011. "The Party Faithful: Partisan Images, Candidate Religion, and the Electoral Impact of Party Identification." American Journal of Political Science. 55 (1): 42–58.

Fiorina, Morris, P., and Samuel J. Abrams. 2008. "Political Polarization in the American Public." Annual Review of Political Science 11 (1): 563-588. Fiorina, Morris P., Samuel J. Abrams, and Jeremy C. Pope. 2011. Culture War? The Myth of Polarized America. Third edition. New York: Pearson. Stavrakakis, Yannis. 2018. "Paradoxes of Polarization: Democracy's Inherent Division and the (Anti-) Populist Challenge." American Behavioral Scientist. 62 (1): 43–58.

clear enemy to take out—the problem is systemic. The political and media industries have simply discovered that the cheapest way to attract our eyeballs and our votes—without awakening our brains—is by dividing us into two roughly equal groups, one that takes the red pill, and the other the blue pill.

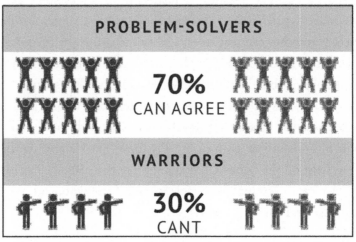

PROBLEM-SOLVERS

70% CAN AGREE

WARRIORS

30% CANT

Both the PROTECTORS and the LIBERATORS have a hard-core "base"— Warriors who champion the core principles and beliefs of conservatives and progressives. About 70% of people are potential "Solution Citizens"—half on the right, half on the left. They can disagree yet find solutions together. About 30% are Warriors—half right and half left. They see each other as enemies, and don't collaborate well.

The reason the media and political industries have settled on separating us into red and blue echo chambers is that it's an effective way to stop change. Machiavelli taught the trick to rulers in fifteenth-century Europe: if a weak leader wants to keep control of a strong-willed population, the most effective way is to divide-and-conquer.

Divide-and-conquer is particularly useful in a democracy. Since a majority is usually needed to sanction major decisions, vested interests learn over time that they can protect the status quo if the public is divided neatly in half. The challenge is how to do it.

Our political parties solved that problem by adopting strategies based on identity politics and wedge issues. Identity politics divides the voting population into narrow categories defined by race, gender, age, belief, or ethnicity. Wedge issues are issues that are intensely divisive—issues that divide people into two camps each holding to opposite positions.

Our two parties pretend to mirror the two worldviews that Americans hold: a conservative worldview focused on protection, and a progressive one focused on liberation. But institutionally, their commitment to these worldviews is rhetorical. Mostly, the parties pander. Republicans pander to Middle Americans, men, older, white, religious, anti-abortion, pro-gun voters. Democrats pander to coastal and big city Americans, women, younger, of color, college-educated, pro-choice, and anti-gun voters. When it comes to policy, they do next to nothing on the issues their voters care about most. Why should they? They need their votes— and the best way to keep them is to deny them what they want. Both Republican and Democratic politicians direct their rhetoric to the voters in their base. But their policies and their allegiance is mostly to interest groups with concentrated money and power.

Before you say "aha! I knew it—our enemy is the rich and powerful," hold your fire. It's more complicated than that.

Thousands of interest groups vie with one another in Washington DC and our 50 state capitals, seeking laws, rules, contracts, and favors that benefit them.[25] There is no Power Elite, Inc. or Deep State LLC. where decisions to oppress us are made. Yes, skillful lobbyists and strategists know how to manipulate the media and public in service to their clients. Corporate lobbyists and government affairs executives aren't trained to help pass needed legislation; their specialty is to "stop or co-opt" new rules that disrupt business-as-usual—block, tackle, or turn every proposal into a benefit. In a way, they have no choice. No single interest group can sacrifice a Congressional perk, unless others do too. We know former executives who have tried, and many others who want to, but can't. Before they can do what's best for the environment and the nation, they need help—your help—to change the rules of the game.

A first step is to understand how the current game is played. It's complicated, but beneath the complexity lies a simple imperative: produce and consume, as much as you can, as if your life depends on it.

That rule—to drive massive consumption of energy and materials

---

25 Nownes, Anthony J. 2013 Interest Groups in American Politics. Routledge: New York.

through the American industrial machine—was embedded into our political and economic system more than 70 years ago, when our nation faced two simultaneous existential threats: the Great Depression and World War II.

The absolute necessity to maximize production to create jobs and win the war led to a formal alliance that has since evolved into what we call The Production Complex. This is an amalgam of corporate, government, labor, military and other institutional interests that President Eisenhower originally called the Military-Industrial Complex back in 1961.[26,27] It has since differentiated into thousands of distinct entities across nearly 100 categories who dominate political and government affairs spending in Washington DC. The Production Complex is no longer a formal alliance. Its founders are long dead. Its offices are dispersed. It has no central headquarters or single trade organization. Instead, it consists of a few hundred core members and an array of others who all benefit by maximizing the production of consumer and military goods. They hire most of the lobbyists, fund most of the think tanks, and pay for most of the polls, focus groups, fundraisers, media consultants, and grassroots organizers who collectively define what is politically feasible in our democracy—what policies and positions our lawmakers are allowed to choose from in the nation's capital. This gives these status quo interest groups effective veto power over ideas that might threaten their long-term hold on power.

Thanks to the Production Complex, America mastered the power of production in the 1940s, and it paid off: we beat the Depression and the fascists. But soon a problem emerged: after the war, economists feared consumption would decline, inviting a new Depression—and the pain of the last one was too great for any politician of either major party to contemplate. So a parallel complex was needed—one that would drive consumption sufficient to keep the wheels of production turning.

The second amalgam of enterprises that profits from a divided

26 The Real News Network. 2011. "Military-Industrial Complex from Eisenhower to Obama." The Real News Network, March 7, 2011, Video, 15:55. https://www.youtube.com/watch?v=AyBelJ85KfY.
27 History.com Editors. 2018. "Military-Industrial Complex." A&E Television Networks, August 21, 2018. https://www.history.com/topics/21st-century/military-industrial-complex#section_4.

electorate is what we call, sensibly enough, the Consumption Complex. These are the media, political, and now technology companies whose common interest is that people consume everything the Production Complex is able to produce and advertise—military, consumer, pharmaceuticals, education, healthy food, junk food, digital media, broadcast media, and popular entertainment of all kinds. The political sector includes the lobbyists, strategists, communications and campaign professionals who feed off the Production Complex, which channels around $12 billion per election cycle through their offices. They spend most of that on the media industry, which complies by organizing voters into left and right-wing segments that can be reached as a group. The third leg of the Consumption Complex is the digital sector, which has grown just as dependent on consumer advertising as traditional media, but lacks the principles of responsible journalism that used to raise their performance above what the market demanded. Now old and new media have mostly capitulated. Fox News panders to the right, while MSNBC and CNN cater to the left—not because most network executives have an ideological agenda, but simply because pretending to have one is so profitable.

Of course, there are corrupt players in politics—plenty of them. But most media, political, and lobbying professionals—even the "good guys"—are just exploiting a corrupted system. It is cheaper, easier, and more profitable in the short term to divide Americans into two tribes, than to manage all our disparate views on a fuller plate of issues.

THE USEFUL IDIOTS

Today, roughly half of the warrior 15% on the right and 15% on the left cling to their views so tightly that they reject alternative points of view before they ever understand them, and prevent others inside their tents to even hear them. These true-believers perform an important service that obviously must have been valuable to our species survival: they ensure that core principles are understood and adhered to and that loyalties, traditions, and alliances valuable to the community are maintained.

But because true-believers are a minority, a democracy should be able to limit their power. This allows the majority to hear clearly expressed but diverse views, and make choices that bend one or both ways.

Unfortunately, however, there are ways to engineer political decision-making to shift power away from the majority, and into the hands of small minorities with rigid and unbending views.

Inside the Warrior communities are a handful of the most aggressive leaders. These are the most polarizing Warriors of all. The Hidden Tribes study suggests they may number 6% of the right and 8% of the left. In our experience, we find them to represent only 3-4% of each - there are always a handful in any convention. But they hit above their weight - hard. They are the charismatic leaders who rile up the Warriors and march them forth to conquer. Vladimir Lenin, the founder of the Soviet Union, has been attributed with using a term for the true-believing Bolshevik leaders whose ideological rigidity and tireless crusading enforced party loyalty in the early days of communist Russia. He called them "useful idiots." Useful Idiots can help mobilize populations toward ends chosen by charismatic leaders. They tend to follow their leaders blindly, rationalizing away any doubts that may emerge along the way.

Before you get the idea that Useful Idiots are a static group of identifiable people, remember this: we are all Useful Idiots, at least occasionally. We all become enamored of certain issues, causes or concerns to the point that our idealistic dedication stretches past our realistic understanding. Useful Idiocy is a quality that varies depending on time, place, and people.

Here in the U.S., political rhetoric is fashioned around the prejudices of two opposing groups of Useful Idiots—one claiming to be conservative and the other progressive. Not everyone on the far ends of the right-to-left spectrum are Useful Idiots. At least not all the time. But among the 15% of Americans at each end of the political spectrum, the most rigid and vocal often fill the Useful Idiot role.

Many of us are fed up with the absolutists on both sides—and how our two parties pander to them. About 40% of us are so disillusioned that we don't identify as Democrats or Republicans.[28] Independents are now the largest, fastest-growing, and most powerless voters in the electorate.

As former Democrats and Republicans declare independence from their parties, they leave the true-believers behind them, including the Useful Idiots so valuable as pawns in the divide-and-conquer strategy. Now that Republican Party registration is declining below 25% of the electorate, and Democrats to below 40%, the Useful Idiots can have their parties to themselves. Even if they're not quite a majority inside their slimmed-down, ideologically-sanitized tents, their rhetoric is expressed with such fierce certainty that most of the others go along. Useful Idiots seem so sure of themselves. And even if they're a little extreme, at least they're our extremists, the rest of us may think. They will create an opening for more reasonable solutions.

This provides a useful advantage to vested interests who benefit from the divide-and-conquer strategy. In Saudi Arabia, the ruling class has a power-sharing arrangement with religious fundamentalists: the ruling family gets the perks of running the kingdom, while the Wahhabi religious leaders take charge of the people. The Wahhabi's teach their fundamentalist beliefs to every Saudi child, to assure that they grow up steeped in the traditions that made the nation, well, a backward-facing monarchy wholly dependent on oil to keep its vulnerable population from perishing beneath the sand.

Similarly, the entrenched interests of the Production and Consumption Complex have cultivated their own sect of Wahhabi-like fundamentalists and empowered them to write the bible that defines the conservative and progressive faiths. Interestingly, the scriptures aren't very complimentary of their institutional benefactors. The left's bible condemns corporate power, while the right's condemns government power. But so long as these two faiths are set against one another, the status quo is safe.

When we travel to Washington DC and meet with political strategists, we're counseled regularly on the game we need to play to pass legislation important to us. And we do play the game. But even if we were

28 Gallup. 2019. "Party Affiliation." Accessed October 24, 2019. https://news.gallup.com/poll/15370/party-affiliation.aspx.

more skilled political practitioners, we'd be hard-pressed to save the planet this way.

That's because the beltway game is mostly about stopping change, not encouraging it. When a company, union, or association hires political strategists and lobbyists, it's usually to stop a legislative or regulatory threat. Government affairs departments serve a risk management role: by stabilizing tax, legislative, and regulatory policy, they help foster a predictable marketplace, which makes investing cheaper and profits surer.

As a result, lobbyists specialize in stopping change. The way they do it is to contribute generously to both political party establishments, so long as the parties keep their voters in tidy right and left echo chambers. Useful Idiots are the unwitting mercenaries that strategists use to enforce loyalty inside the party and keep less doctrinaire voters from straying. Strategists craft simpleton "narratives" that appeal to party stalwarts and reinforce the core beliefs of the ideological left and ideological right. In narratives aimed at progressives, they cast corporations as the demons. In narratives to conservatives, government plays that role. The idiots then make themselves useful by imposing ideological litmus tests on those on their side of the spectrum who are less certain of their beliefs. Destroy the corporate oppressors, the extreme left Warriors demand. Destroy the government oppressors, their right-wing counterparts insist. Since each side communicates only with their own political tribe, they each build movements that rhetorically reflect their extremes, but lack the power to carry out their lopsided agendas.

The progressive left—determinedly anti-corporate—demands that the government step in and control corporate abuse. The conservative— just as solidly anti-government—demands that corporations step in and take over government functions. Neither seems to realize there's a third option: empower people instead. They can't even imagine what that means—they're so used to their institutional dependency. The result is a convenient one for big corporations, big government, and the combined power of a corporate state.

Before you go hating on corporations or government, however, please resist that trap. Hating an institution is like despising a needle-nose plier. It's just a tool. Don't yell at it. Use it.

Big corporations and big government have big roles to play. They help us serve our needs. They abuse us precisely when we mistake them for people. We may think of them as our masters or our caretakers. They are neither.

Our news media don't help. Gone are the days when broadcasters were nominally objective, and networks could take a financial loss to deliver quality news programs.[29] Today journalism has devolved into entertainment, with one objective paramount: get us to buy stuff.

We all experience how this works. The major broadcast and digital news sources—Fox News, MSNBC, CNN, Google, and Facebook—each divide Americans into non-overlapping tribes of either conservatives or liberals, and present us with standardized news feeds that stick mostly to one of two dominant narratives. Conservatives watch Fox News, where they learn over-and-over that the liberal Deep State is stealing money and power from individuals and transferring it to the government.[30] Then conservatives open their laptops where their fears are validated and heightened by digital tweets, Google searches and Facebook posts that reinforce their preconceptions.

Liberals, meanwhile, watch MSNBC, where they hear repeatedly that greedy corporations and super-wealthy business titans are shifting money and power from the people to their own pockets.[31] Then when they turn to their iPhones, they are fed tweets, posts, and breaking news alerts that reinforce their fear of corporations and the wealthy. Government, they learn, can be their noble savior, once the true progressive majority congeals into a solid mass and takes control.

If Fox News is worried that big government is taking power from

29 Gunther, Marc. 1999. "The Transformation of Network News." Nieman Reports, June 15, 1999. https://niemanreports.org/articles/the-transformation-of-network-news/.
30 Fox News. "What is the 'Deep State?'" Fox News, January 5, 2018. Video, 1:54. https://www.youtube.com/watch?v=JNiyKT_TCxQ.
31 MSNBC. 2016. "DiCaprio Criticizes Energy Industry's 'Corporate Greed'." MSNBC, January 22, 2016. https://www.msnbc.com/msnbc/watch/dicaprio-attacks-energys-corporate-greed-606804035640.

people, and MSNBC about big corporations doing the same, where is the network calling attention to both?

It doesn't exist. Why not? Because let's face it, media companies are not primarily interested in the health of our democracy. They don't care too much whether government and corporations are growing more powerful, and individuals less so. They are mostly interested in selling advertisements to companies that want our consumer dollars, and political interest groups who want our tax dollars. For that, the simplest narratives are the best. Complex realities about well-intentioned people doing inadvertent harm cause us to think critically—not a useful quality when the ads come on.

We're not demonizing government or corporations here. We are pro-government and pro-business. They each play essential roles in a healthy democracy and economy. We're just looking realistically at the incentives that corporations, government, and their dependents currently face to maximize their own shared power and profit.

Fox, CNN, MSNBC, Google, and Facebook are not fundamentally news or media companies. They are advertising companies. Their business objective is to sell advertising and marketing data to companies and, during campaign season, to political action committees (PACs). The companies want us to buy their products and services, to keep the Production Machine operating at full power. The PACs want us to buy their ideas and elect the politicians they trust, so the Consumption Machine can suck up as much of our economic and ecological resources as possible.

How do advertisers convince consumers to give them our dollars? It's a pain-and-pleasure business model. Media companies offer us pain, with entertainment that triggers feelings of inadequacy and news stories that make us feel unhappy or fearful, victimized or threatened by demons we've come to expect—say, big oil companies, criminal aliens, oppressive bureaucrats, greedy businessmen, conservative bigots, or progressive spendthrifts. They then turn on the offers of pleasure, luring us with products, services, and politicians that promise protection, diversion, and wealth. The "news and entertainment" fosters insecurity and fear. The advertising offers us relief and the prospect of pleasure.

Sean Hannity and Rachel Maddow may be quite sincere when each of them warns us about the Useful Idiots on the other side of the political divide. Some of their warnings are valid. But they aren't hired to alert us. They are hired to attract us. We are the product that they are delivering to their real customer: the Consumption Complex. Sean and Rachel keep their seats by keeping us in ours.

Why isn't there public demand for an alternative to the fear-and-hate model for politics and media? There is. Fully 70% of us don't fear and hate the people on the "other side," until we are taught to. Seven-in-ten Americans, from the political left to the right, can listen to each other, work out our differences, and agree on solutions. Local and subscription-based media mostly appeal to this broader base, and are much less exploitive of our impulses and fears. But today's global media, driven at the speed of data, find it simpler to appeal to our worst instincts, and profit from the ad sales they can generate.

We understand why. If political and media strategists appealed to both the left and right together, conservatives and progressives could combine their warnings into one: government and corporate power are both out of control. Big spending—economic, social, and ecological—is way beyond what we can sustain. The combined effect is that money and power are being siphoned quickly away from people, and channeled into institutions that claim to represent our best interests. If they could rise above their fears, the left and right could join forces and reverse the flow.

But that's not appealing to advertisers who want more consumer dollars, or interest groups that want more taxpayer dollars. If the political right and left joined to rein in the orgy of spending that threatens our pocketbooks and our planet, that would restrict the flow of money to entrenched institutions and the political and media interests that serve them.

A better strategy, for status quo interest groups, would be to convince conservatives that government is the enemy—and that by joining forces with corporations, they can cut taxes but keep on spending plenty for the military and defense needs that keep us safe. Then convince liberals that corporations are the enemy—and by joining forces with government, they can regulate, punish, and tax them, all while shifting more money to the contractors and companies that will meet our health and social needs. That keeps the public hating and spending. What could be better?

Some of us are beginning to tire of the ploy, however. We love free enterprise and democratic government, for example. But as much as we love the people we know inside big corporate and government institutions, we know they don't always have the power alone to mobilize their institutions for good.

Why do we know this? Because business and political leaders tell us so. Repeatedly. Fervently. Big corporations can't reliably act in the public interest, without an active and informed citizenry that sets expectations well above what the market will accept. And big government agencies become self-absorbed bureaucracies without citizens actively engaged to keep them accountable.

It seems obvious that we need to decentralize the power of both big government and big business. But it's hard for conservatives and progressives to join forces for their common good. They see the world differently, and their preconceptions foster undue sympathy for government by the left, and undue sympathy for business on the right. Each would rather forge partnerships with their least-unfavored institution than hold hands with each other.

These two worldviews set us up for conflict, but also enable us to coalesce and work together. Take the way we approach environmental protection. Liberals often believe nature is pretty much perfect as is—they take a preservationist approach: leave nature alone! She'll serve life best if we just let her be. Their idealized view of nature is the rainforest—a place of incredible diversity where millions of species of plants and animals live in balance and harmony. To them, human interference in nature is mostly unnatural, and morally questionable. Only indigenous communities living traditional hunter-gatherer lifestyles are truly living in alignment with nature. Modern society, with our big extractive technologies run by giant impersonal corporations, inherently disrupts nature's sacred balance.

Conservatives, on the other hand, tend to see nature as a place of both risks and opportunities. They take a conservationist approach: let's be stewards of our lands, maintaining their health and productive capacity, while reducing the dangers that sometimes lurk there. What liberals call rainforests conservatives call jungles: places where myriad strange creatures live in competition with one another for scarce resources. It's an eat-or-be-eaten world they see out there, and given the choice, they like our place at the top of the food chain. Humans can't leave nature alone if we want to survive—we have to take our place within it, managing our natural lands as virtuous stewards, enhancing their value to people. To conservatives, human interference in nature is natural, and morally righteous. Nature provides resources that enable us to thrive. We serve nature best by succeeding in this competition among the species.

Both make valid points. Together, these two halves of the environmental movement can serve both people and nature well. Until the 1980s, the left and right overcame most of their differences and worked closely together both to preserve and conserve nature. This partnership was difficult at times, but healthy for all.

Not anymore. Today, the environment has become a partisan issue. Democrats own the "for" side, claiming to champion liberal preservationist ideals. Republicans own the "against" side, claiming nature is a well-stocked warehouse and we don't need to conserve it any more than we already are. This division carries a few costs we probably don't want to bear, like economic stagnation, ecological decline, and ultimately, if we do little, our own demise as a species.

To avoid that, it's important to restore the natural balance that brought our two movements together in past decades to protect nature, both as a sacred space to preserve and a useful one to conserve.

CHAPTER THREE
BLIND IN BOTH EYES

CLIMATE DENIAL, LEFT AND RIGHT

There are two kinds of climate denial, one conservative and the other progressive.

Conservative climate denial goes something like this: Scientists tell us that, to avoid climate catastrophe, we need big government to limit our freedom and prosperity to protect life on earth. As conservatives, we hate big government, and love freedom, prosperity, and the free markets that bring them. If the science requires we sacrifice that, the science must be wrong.

Progressive climate denial goes something like this: Scientists tell us that, to avoid climate catastrophe, we need big government to limit corporate power and protect life on earth. As progressives, we hate big corporations, and love the shared sustainable prosperity that government can require of them. If the science requires that we regulate corporations, the science must be right.

Neither science nor logic tell us any of that. They indicate that climate change is real, human-caused, and potentially catastrophic. But they don't conclusively tell us what to do about it, or the roles big corporations or big government should play.

Conveniently, however, both narratives deliver enormous profits to political and media power brokers. First, they keep the two sides at war, one fighting for freedom and prosperity, the other for justice and fairness.

Second, they guarantee that no matter which side prevails, the status quo will broker the deal.

There was a time when conservatives and progressives could each see half of the reality we face. Conservatives, with only their right eye open, could see that we are out of money and deep in debt. Progressives, with their left eye open, could see that we cannot pay off our debt by extracting it from the poor, the middle class, or the environment. Put our left and right vision together, and most of us could see what was going on. Both sides are correct. We are going bankrupt - our economic and ecological spending are both out of control.

But living within our means is dangerous to a political and media system that thrives by skimming its share from the massive flow of power from nature and people to big corporations and big government. So long as the left denies economic debt and the right denies ecological debt, no governing majority can emerge to challenge uncontrolled spending. Power brokers decide what is politically feasible, and care little whether they call it capitalism or socialism. Their cash cow is the corporate state.

So how do we get our power back from them? The first step is to realize there is no them. Corporations and governments are not people. They are institutions, legal constructs we create so we can better serve each other.

People pay taxes to government, to pay other people and corporations for services. We pay corporations so they will pay other people and government for more products and services. When people demand more but won't spend the money for it, our institutions have ways to make us pay anyway. They borrow the money, usually from other institutions. Then, because institutions aren't people, people are responsible for the debt.

Officially, the national debt of the United States exceeded $23 trillion in February 2020. But we actually owe, some estimates say, more than 50 trillion dollars[32] in government debts to ourselves—debts we will need to repay in the next couple of generations. How will we pay those debts

---

32 For an explanation of the measurement of debt on an accrual versus cash basis, see: Pethokoukis, James. 2012. "The National Debt Isn't $15 Trillion. It's $50 Trillion," AEI, June 5, 2012. https://www. aei.org/economics/the-national-debt-isnt-15-trillion-its-50-trillion/.

back? Many say it doesn't really matter since the debts are to ourselves. But are they?

Really, the debts are to our institutions.[33] We owe domestic and international corporations, governments, NGOs, wealthy families, and all of the institutions of the political media money machine, all the money that they have spent on our behalf. To pay them back, we now owe them our work, and our children's work. We owe them a generous portion of our current and future labor, earnings, and savings, so that they can continue to provide the services that they perform for us. The question is, do we really think they're doing as good a job at providing for our needs if in the process they have rung up this level of debt on our behalf?

At 50 trillion dollars, the debt now equals about $153,000[34] per man, woman, and child in the U.S. If you're a family of four, that's about $600,000 in debt. Different economists measure the debt differently, so you could cut that number in half or even by 75%.[35] It's still daunting. And it is not just theoretical. It is on the ledgers. We are indentured servants to our institutional selves. In the next two or three generations, we will have to work very, very hard to pay ourselves back for all the services provided for us in the past.

What does it mean when our individual selves owe money to our institutional selves? It means that other people—the ones in control of each institution's purse strings—will decide just how much we will work and pay in return for the services they have provided us. Because these institutions are our employers and our enforcers. They are our government agencies. They are our labor unions. They are the retailers and brands that provide us with consumer products, the suppliers that extract and process the energy and resources we use. They are the media companies that program us to consume what we produce. And they are the political strategists that convince us to keep it all in place, mostly as-is.

---

33 U.S. Government Accountability Office. 2019. "America's Fiscal Future." Accessed November 5, 2019. https://www.gao.gov/americas_fiscal_future?t=federal_debt.
34 This number was calculated using the 2018 population estimate from: https://www.census.gov/quickfacts/fact/table/US/PST045218.
35 Adkins, Troy. 2019. "What the National Debt Means to You." Investopedia, May 13, 2019. https://www.investopedia.com/articles/economics/10/national-debt.asp.

Have you ever wondered how it is that we've become so enormously rich since World War II, and yet we seem to be working harder than ever to make ends meet? A big part of it is that people are not represented by this political media money machine—only our institutions are. Consequently, those in charge of the institutions keep running up their tabs then passing the invoice to us as debt. And we keep working hard to pay it back to them, because we don't see the connection between our hard work and their big spending. After all, they're spending it for us.

We also don't understand why money seems to be concentrating in the hands of a few—mostly institutions and those inside the institutions with the opportunity to scoop up a percentage or two as it flows past them. If you're on the left, you might want to blame the bankers, the executives, and the billionaires. If you're on the right, you might want to blame the public employee unions, the government bureaucrats, and the career politicians. That's who you are supposed to blame. These are the demons assigned to you, as loyal progressives or conservatives. The problem is that none of these people or the institutions they run have the power by themselves to reboot the political and media machine. We've worked with them all, and we've seen many make the attempt. Try as they might to fundamentally challenge the duopoly they depend on, they inevitably learn that by themselves, they only have the power to exploit it. So many do.

But many right and left leaders are wrong about what to do. To stimulate new growth, many on the right would drill baby drill the nation's limited energy resources, as fast as we can, while many on the left would spend baby spend financial resources the nation does not have, as fast as we can, and then pay off our growing debts by printing more money.

Each of these is a false panacea. One spends down our economic prosperity. The other builds up our ecological debt.

The real way to end the two deficits is not to consume value. It is to create it, by tapping the power of people and business to innovate. But for that to happen, we need to overcome the gridlock that divides the left and right, to embed old ways of doing business by law and regulation.

The right looks at the left's denial of economic limits, and figures they must be either evil or insane. The left looks at the right's use of military might to support our dependence on fossil fuels, and their denial of environmental and climate impacts, and figures they must be perverse and corrupt.

The left and right rationalize their respective blind spots by embracing the groupthink cultivated by political forces seeking to win the next election on behalf of their party or interest group. But since there is always a "next election," their process of power-jockeying never seems to end.

Neither party's power brokers are willing to dispense with the hope that, in less than two years, they will finally achieve a permanent political victory over their ideological foes.

Smart people on both sides know that the rationales are false. But when brave ones point this out, they risk being ostracized by forces within each. Economist Bruce Bartlett, a policy advisor to the Reagan and George H. W. Bush administrations, has grown weary of the false debate. In his book, The Benefit and The Burden: Tax Reform—Why We Need It and What It Will Take, he describes the futility of massive cuts in federal spending.[36]

The national debt, Bartlett says, is like a bank loan—it must be paid off in installments, out of current income. It is a part of our government debt, but only a small part. The vast majority comes in the form of political commitments we have made to important constituencies: future benefits to retired federal employees, veterans, and Social Security and Medicare recipients. These must be paid only when they come due, so they do not appear in the federal budget, and are almost never counted when we measure the government debt.

That is because the government does its accounting on a cash basis, not an accrual basis, the way corporations do.[37]

36 Bartlett, Bruce. 2012. The Benefit and The Burden: Tax Reform-Why We Need It and What It Will Take. New York: Simon & Schuster.
37 Morah, Chizoba. 2019. "How Does Accrual Accounting Differ from Cash Basis Accounting?" Investopedia, June 25, 2019. https://www.investopedia.com/ask/answers/09/accrual-accounting.asp.

That way, it can avoid booking the full cost of its programs annually. Instead, the government publishes a separate, obscure financial statement, now called the Financial Report of the United States Government.[38]

The Obama administration published the fiscal 2011 version on December 23, two days before Christmas, while reporters were probably too busy preparing for the holidays to read a complex 254-page financial document.[39] Neither the New York Times nor Fox News seemed to notice it.

But Bartlett did. Altogether, he found, the Treasury reported the government's total indebtedness at $51.3 trillion.[40]

The national debt made up a fifth of this—$10.2 trillion. Veterans and federal employees were owed $5.8 trillion. Social Security's unfunded liability—promised benefits over expected Social Security revenues—was $9.2 trillion over the next 75 years. And Medicare's unfunded liability was estimated to be $24.6 trillion.

At the time, this debt totaled nearly the entire net worth of all American households, and it continues to rise. It would be impossible to cut spending enough for a single generation of Americans to pay it off.

Unless our productivity and output grows, the Congressional Budget Office projects that within 20 years the federal debt will rise to over 110 percent of GDP, as our future commitments come due, and suddenly become part of the nation's acknowledged debt.[41]

This will have a devastating financial impact on the nation. Balancing the federal budget will not be nearly enough, as Bartlett and other economists document. The federal government would have to run a substantial surplus continuously for 75 years just to prevent the debt to GDP ratio from rising.[42]

38 Bureau of the Fiscal Service. 2018. "Financial Report of the United States Government." Accessed November 5, 2019. https://fiscal.treasury.gov/reports-statements/financial-report/.

39 Bureau of the Fiscal Service. 2011. "Citizen's Guide to the 2011 Financial Report of the United States Government." Accessed November 5, 2019. https://fiscal.treasury.gov/files/reports-statements/financial-report/11frusg.pdf.

40 Bartlett, Bruce. 2012. "The True Federal Debt." Economix, The New York Times, January 3, 2012. https://economix.blogs.nytimes.com/2012/01/03/the-true-federal-debt/.

41 Topoleski, Julie. 2014. "Growing Deficits Over the Long Term Would Cause Federal Debt to Exceed 100 Percent of GDP by 2039." Congressional Budget Office, July 21, 2014. https://www.cbo.gov/publication/45555.

42n Bartlett, Bruce. 2012. "The True Federal Debt." Economix, The New York Times, January 3, 2012. https://economix.blogs.nytimes.com/2012/01/03/the-true-federal-debt/.

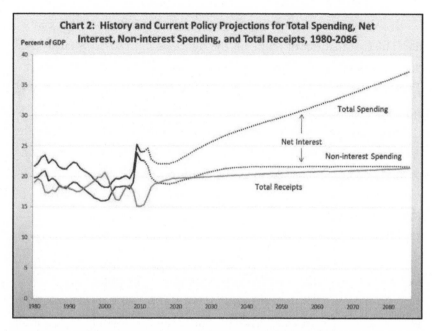

Source: Bureau of the Fiscal Service. 2011. "Citizen's Guide to the 2011 Financial Report of the United States Government." Accessed November 5, 2019. https://fiscal.treasury.gov/files/reports-statements/financial-report/11frusg.pdf.

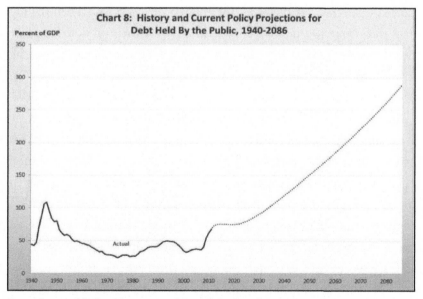

Source: Bureau of the Fiscal Service. 2011. "Citizen's Guide to the 2011 Financial Report of the United States Government." Accessed November 5, 2019. https://fiscal.treasury.gov/files/reports-statements/financial-report/11frusg.pdf.

If we cannot cut spending enough to erase the deficit, what can we do? The first instinct of many on the right has been to do what worked during periods of continuous growth: consume more fossil fuel energy. That prescription not only seems to advance their mission, but also appeals to an array of business, labor, and investor interests.

But that path is well worn. It has been almost fifty years since the first global energy crisis in 1973. Since that time, rather than innovating beyond our dependence on fossil fuels, the right has focused on building our military power, enabling us to intervene, to protect our sources of supply and to prevent disruptions.

We have as a consequence sacrificed $7 trillion in domestic growth, to fund our foreign oil habit. We have transferred over $1.2 trillion to nations that are either unstable or antithetical to our interests.

Those dollars may have financed the Baathist terrorists under Saddam Hussein in Iraq, the radical Mullahs under the Ayatollah in Iran, and of course al-Qaeda. In Saudi Arabia, al-Qaeda terrorists were so infuriated by the presence of US military on Saudi soil, that they focused their oil-financed operation on throwing the infidels off their soil. Then, failing that, they came to our soil. They used a few of their oil dollars to buy airline tickets in 2001, and took out the World Trade Center, and along with almost 3,000 lives.

The other panacea of some on the right is to drill our way out of debt. In this view, the U.S. can simply embark on massive and permanently increasing extraction of fossil fuels, all from within our borders. The U.S. may not be as rich as others in oil, but it does have vast holdings of natural gas, enough to largely replace our highly polluting stocks of coal, which are being depleted more quickly than once thought. Some on the left would lock these reserves away forever, to avoid the risks of hydrological fracturing. Some on the right would open them up completely, avoiding regulations designed to protect public health and the environment.

The better approach is for the left and right to work together to set smart standards for natural gas production, to reduce U.S. dependence on imported oil and dirtier coal, and to protect our air, water, and land.

The nation should neither lock away nor quickly deplete our natural gas reserves. It should use them prudently to help us transition to the next energy economy.

The right's insistence on its fiction, that we needn't worry about fossil fuel dependence, undermines what it cherishes most, including the nation's security, prosperity, and freedom.

The left's insistence on its fiction, that we needn't worry about massive government spending and control, undermines what it cherishes most, including economic fairness and freedom from injustice.

Much as the right might wish, it is impossible to cut or drill enough to pay our debt. Our politicians, in order to serve federal employees, veterans, retirees, and other interest groups, have leveraged the whole economy, placing us at the mercy of some of the world's most threatening nations. Most future spending will not be for programs with current or future value, but for interest on debt. The costs will be more than just economic.

Much as the left might wish, we can't just print more money, and erase the paper debt as it comes due. Flooding the world economy with dollars that have not been earned creates no real value. It will not actually put food on our tables or a roof over our heads. Instead, it will spur more spending, both economic and environmental. Any short-term increases in prosperity will dissipate, either through inflation, new debt, or ecological degradation.

The reality that neither the left nor the right, each spun by their numerous power brokers, want to face is this: we simply cannot cut, drill, or spend our way to prosperity. It is impossible to live off subsidies forever. Eventually, someone has to create real value.

CHAPTER FOUR

HAVE WE LOST
OUR MARBLE?

WHY "GLOOM AND DOOM" ENVIRONMENTALISM SHRINKS OUR SUPPORT BASE, FUNDS OUR OPPONENTS, AND FAILS TO DELIVER THE SOLUTIONS WE NEED

On September 23, 2019, we watched on our iPhones as 16-year-old Swedish climate activist Greta Thunberg mounted the stage at the United Nations Climate Action Summit, and told world leaders, "How dare you, you have stolen my dreams and my childhood with your empty words."[43]

Even in Dallas, school children had gathered at street corners in support of Greta's message. Millions around the world, including 1.1 million in New York City alone, skipped school that day to deliver a similarly well-deserved scolding to their parents and older folks for climate malfeasance at 3,000 rallies in over 150 countries.[44]

We felt ashamed, of course, but that's nothing new. We've felt shame all our lives, starting 50 years ago when on the first Earth Day we blamed our elders, and soon ourselves, for wrecking the planet.

Greta first gained media attention as a determined Swedish activist who boycotted school to call attention to the climate crisis. Her early U.S.

---

43 Thunberg, Greta. "Greta Thunberg (Young Climate Activist) at the Climate Action Summit 2019 - Official Video. " United Nations. Video, 4:07. https://www.youtube.com/watch?v=u9KxE4Kv9A8.
44 Parker, Laura. 2019. "'Listen and Help Us': Kids Worldwide Are on Strike for the Climate." National Geographic, September 20, 2019. https://www.nationalgeographic.com/environment/2019/09/kids-march-climate-action/.

media appearances were calm and persuasive, and drew modest attention. At the U.N., she added anger and disgust to her repertoire—and the media loved it. Even before Greta finished her remarks, the contrarian Tweet storm had begun. Our iPhones were chirping with breaking news alerts, fervent commentary, and well-timed money requests from candidates and non-profits with opinions to share.

It wasn't Greenpeace or Friends of the Earth reaching out to us. It was self-described "conservative" campaigns and non-profits, who cast young Greta as an angry suicidal heavy metal rock star, and her followers as unwitting pawns of angry left-wing extremists determined to subvert capitalism, ruin our economy, and steal our children's future.

It wasn't the first time. When over 300,000 pro-climate activists descended on New York City in September 2014, our media trackers detected an immediate uptick in activity.[45] Tweets, posts, and dollars started to flow in, by the thousands, as concerned citizens registered their worries. Much of the outpouring was by climate skeptics and their supporters, who spread the word that environmental "extremists" were taking to the streets, fomenting climate fears to drive their "real" agenda: a big government takeover of the market economy.

These two instances tell why climate champions need to change our tactics. We're not proposing that we stop taking public action. But we are proposing a change in how. "Gloom-and-doom" environmentalism—our movement's overwhelming focus on blaming each other for the catastrophic consequences that we can expect from global climate collapse, unless we take urgent action—is now one of the most powerful agents driving opposition to our movement. Our negative mindset could soon become a self-fulfilling prophecy, one that undermines the faith, will, and confidence of the public to take the steps necessary to protect our climate.

It is time to shift gears, from our dependence on gloom, doom, blame, and shame, to a vision of what is possible, desirable, and within reach.

This is not a call for denial. There is plenty of cause for alarm. In

---

45 Restuccia, Andrew. 2014. "Greens: Climate March Breaks Record." Politico, September, 21, 2014, updated September 22. https://www.politico.com/story/2014/09/peoples-climate-march-nyc-111177.

the industrial era, human actions have driven atmospheric carbon dioxide concentrations to the highest known level on our planet since the Pliocene Epoch millions of years ago, long before the age of humans.[46] This rise will doubtless continue for generations.[47]

Fear is justified. Panic is not. Fear serves us in one way: to wake us up, and call our attention to a threat. After that, it loses its utility. It freezes us in place. The layering of fear on fear, so quickly we numb to it, stops us from acting. Our anxiety has no place to go.

One way to direct our fear is to hate. This can be functional, if we hate we must kill. Hate strips away human empathy, and allows us to destroy what threatens us, as if we were a machine.

But here too, hate is only useful if it is directed toward a genuine demon, a threat that must be destroyed. Otherwise, the hate dehumanizes us precisely when we most need to be human. It deactivates our capacity to understand at the very moment we most need to understand. Like now.

We don't deny the utility of fear and hate. We simply notice that our fears are being continuously triggered, directing our hate toward the wrong enemy.

We have a choice. We can behave like Useful Idiots, and champion climate fundamentalism. That will keep us in fundamental gridlock, dependent on big vested interests on both the left and right, who want to lock in old-style industrial-based growth and pave a path back to the consumption-driven economy of the 1950s through 1970s.

---

46 NASA Global Climate Change. 2019. "Graphic: Carbon Dioxide Hits New High." Accessed November 6, 2019. https://climate.nasa.gov/climate_resources/7/graphic-carbon-dioxide-hits-new-high/.
47 IPCC (Intergovernmental Panel on Climate Change). 2014. Climate Change 2014: Synthesis Report. Contribution of Working Groups I, II and III to the Fifth Assessment Report of the Intergovernmental Panel on Climate Change. Core Writing Team, R.K. Pachauri and L.A. Meyer (editors). Geneva, Switzerland: IPCC. https://www.ipcc.ch/report/ar5/syr/.

NEW YORK TIMES MAGAZINE, AUGUST 1, 2018

"The world has warmed more than one degree Celsius since the Industrial Revolution. The Paris climate agreement — the nonbinding, unenforceable and already unheeded treaty signed on Earth Day in 2016 — hoped to restrict warming to two degrees. The odds of succeeding, according to a recent study based on current emissions trends, are one in 20. If by some miracle we are able to limit warming to two degrees, we will only have to negotiate the extinction of the world's tropical reefs, sea-level rise of several meters and the abandonment of the Persian Gulf. The climate scientist James Hansen has called two-degree warming "a prescription for long-term disaster." Long-term disaster is now the best-case scenario. Three-degree warming is a prescription for short-term disaster: forests in the Arctic and the loss of most coastal cities. Robert Watson, a former director of the United Nations Intergovernmental Panel on Climate Change, has argued that three-degree warming is the realistic minimum. Four degrees: Europe in permanent drought; vast areas of China, India and Bangladesh claimed by desert; Polynesia swallowed by the sea; the Colorado River thinned to a trickle; the American Southwest largely uninhabitable. The prospect of a five-degree warming has prompted some of the world's leading climate scientists to warn of the end of human civilization."

Rich, Nathaniel. "Losing Earth: The Decade We Almost Stopped Climate Change." The New York Times Magazine, August 1, 2018.

Or, we can step around those vested interests—of which we are all a part—and continue on the path that is forming ahead of us. A path along which we begin to empower not the big institutions of the past century, but people, so that we draw from inside ourselves the creative capacities that can support our species in the centuries to come.

For inspiration on how to do so, we look to the ideas and insights of optimistic environmentalists from the years before cynics turned the planet into a partisan cause, smart scientists who see the risks but also sense the possibilities of our present predicament. People like William McDonough, who sees our capacity to create value by design; Amory Lovins, who wants us to reinvent fire; and Janine Benyus, who knows nature not as a source of fuels to be extracted and used up, but as a source of ideas and innovations that we can mimic.[48,49,50]

We also gain inspiration from the possibilities recently unleashed in our economy and culture, through which we are just beginning to take steps beyond the merely industrial. The digital age, with all its many faults, has cultivated a kind of growth founded not on fossil fuels and raw materials, but on knowledge and smart design. An economy in which productivity gains can happen not in increments of a percent or two, but in leapfrog advances that multiply many times the amount of value we tap from a given amount of fuel or material. And a culture that values people not as mere consumers whose footprints on the planet must be driven toward zero, but as creators who contribute value to the whole, whose footprints leave a positive impression on the earth.

Last century, industrialism succeeded in making us materially prosperous, by expanding the productivity of our labor at just 3 percent per year, on average. In the course of a century, that enabled us to gain 14 times as much material benefit from every hour we worked, compared with the beginning of the century.

In the west, those machines made most of us rich, in physical terms. They solved the production problem that had destined most of humanity to lives of bare sustenance in all prior generations.

48 McDonough, William. 2019. "About." Accessed November 6, 2019. https://www.mcdonough.com/.

49 Lovins, Amory. 2014. "Reinventing Fire." Accessed November 6, 2019. https://rmi.org/insight/reinventing-fire/.

50 Biomimicry Institute. 2019. "Janine Benyus." Accessed November 6, 2019. https://biomimicry.org/janine-benyus/.

But there was a price to prosperity. The first price we paid was our autonomy, our control over our own lives. We had to sacrifice a bit of our autonomy, to realize our prosperity. We had to work in factories, offices, and assembly lines, and become small parts in large industrial enterprises. Except for a few of us, no longer could we be artisans, creators, hunters, and builders, contributing holistically to small communities of people we knew, people who could appreciate our contributions. Instead, we became generic producers and consumers, in neighborhoods where most of those around us were anonymous to us, and disconnected from us, and where we all grew dependent on big government, big corporations, big labor, and professional institutions, to whom we gave our power.

This diminished us in many ways, but the trade was worthwhile, because together we built a civilization with which we could feed and nourish not only our bodies, but also our minds and ultimately, we suspect, our hearts. And from this experience, we now have the knowledge and technological capacity to amply provide for our material needs—to provide the food, clothing, and shelter we all need to support our lives, and do something worthwhile with them.

Moreover, we have also birthed a set of digital technologies that can reverse the flow of power, from the vast industrial institutions of our recent past, back to the communities, families, and individuals that sacrificed their power and their sense of connection for the greater good.

Those technologies could drive broader gains in productivity than anything we experienced in the industrial age. Because they are founded on knowledge, they can increase the productivity not just of labor but also of energy and materials—of our treasured natural resources—by much more than today's 1 or 2 percent a year, and perhaps significantly beyond last century's 3 percent rates.[51] Instead of working less and consuming more, they can drive productivity gains that enable us to consume less while prospering more.

That is an essential ingredient in sustainable prosperity. Because if we can grow productivity faster than we grow our economy, we can

---

51 Sprague, Shawn. 2017. "Below Trend: The U.S. Productivity Slowdown Since the Great Recession." Productivity January 2017 6, no. 2 (January): 1-12.

enhance and expand global prosperity, even as we reduce our draws on the fossil fuels and raw materials that lie beneath the surface of the earth—and reduce our destructive greenhouse gas emissions into our shared atmosphere.

More exciting to us, however, is that by using these same technologies, we can begin to repair the connections between people, which were severed in the industrial era; to reawaken our sense of self and community. This is a far cry from what those technologies seem to be doing to us now. They have divided us more than ever, into digital tribes and solitary individuals who engage in rhetorical wars with an impulsivity that can be dangerous. But people can reverse this power dynamic, and take greater control of these technologies, not by enlisting the support of government, but by joining together as organized citizens.

Examine the underlying drivers behind each movement in politics today, and you will find that each is, in part, an effort to move past industrial alienation and consumerism, toward a better future in which we are both more prosperous and more connected. From the progressive and environmental movements mostly on the left, to the religious, fiscal, and free market libertarian conservatives on the right, we see efforts to restore what we lost in the industrial era, and develop a post-industrial, post-consumerist, post-materialist, post-big government, post-big corporate culture.

Each of these movements sees an inhumane and unsustainable aspect of our current system. Each seeks in some way to reconnect us with our roots, with a core aspect of ourselves that is not just material in form. Environmentalists see the foolishness of endless fossil fuel extraction, but our movement is also a spiritual one, in which we seek to recognize the sacredness of the earth. Progressives see the injustice of income inequality and corporate power in a world where global labor unions are simply not feasible, but they also yearn for a renewed sense of connection and community, a return to the village.

Religious conservatives see how a consumer society discounts the value of life. They rebel against the mechanistic view of the nature of life that blinds us to the miracle of the creation moment. Political conservatives decry the loss of individual power as big governments and big corporations grow mutually dependent, and also seek to remind us of the wisdom embedded in many of our longstanding traditions. Conservatives believe America's commitment to freedom is real and worth preserving, and want us to respect the sacrifices made to secure liberty on our behalf. Free market libertarians sense that the economy, too, is like a creative natural ecosystem; they want us to understand that, like nature, it is something precious that can be destroyed if we seek cavalierly to dam it, control it, and destroy its diversity.

Each of these movements is a combination of purpose and power. The purposes of each are linked—they all contribute to restoring and enhancing the humanity of our productive system. But the power of each, paradoxically, is built in significant part by doing the opposite—by demonizing those who are members of the other movements, the other tribes. Each movement now builds its power by attacking the humanity of the others, and in the process sacrifices a part of its own humanity and its deeper purpose. Each sees its political priorities in narrow litmus-tested terms incompatible with those of the others. Each, as a consequence, may be manipulated and exploited by a myriad political and communications strategists, who fan the flames of demonization and outrage to either pass a law that advantages them or, more often, protect some advantage the political process has granted them in the past.

There was a time when it was appropriate for these movements to see one another as adversaries, because the system as a whole would reconcile their differences and enable us to advance. But today, their battles are largely contrived and perpetuated, not to advance one over the other, but to keep them all at war, so they can never bring their parts together to form a more powerful whole, one which could indeed help us overcome the ecological, economic, and spiritual resistance that is a natural part of the birth of a new system.

Enabling the emergence of something new does require a willingness to let go of something old. In this case, we all—and those in these parallel movements as well—need to let go of certain assumptions which lock us into our consumptive, non-sustainable, big institution dependent, power centralizing past:

First, we must let go of our perceived political demon-enemies—those whose words and deeds, though nonviolent, seem antithetical to our interests. We must not be affected by their demonization of us, other than to see what they truly want us to understand. And we must cease to demonize them, or they will never understand us.

Second, we must change our policy strategy, from one that seeks to forcibly "command-and-control" a sustainable economy into existence, to a set of policies that successfully wean us off our dependencies, and cultivate sustainable prosperity the way nature itself does, through feedback-and-adaptation.

Third, we must change our political coalition, from one that pits a small set of activists, donors, and green business interests against a much bigger and more powerful one, to a new coalition in which we join with parallel movements that include the left and right, religious and spiritual, digital and manufacturing sectors, major brands, and even giant oil, gas, and mining companies that know they can and will change.

Fourth, we must recognize that the core objectives of our most passionate adversaries are actually the missing pieces that enable our success. They are intrinsic not just to our political success, but to the success of a culture of sustainable prosperity.

We need to hear the religious conservatives when they plead with us to see the sacred in life; the political conservatives when they point to the wisdom of self-discipline and tradition; the Tea Party when they remind us that freedom is our nation's core purpose; the libertarian community when they point to the creative wonders of markets. We know they are hypocritical, and they know we are—we're all human. But as we begin to hear them, they will begin to hear us. They will begin to see how today's economic injustices and ecological exploitation run counter to their ideals of life, liberty, tradition, fiscal sanity, spiritual sanctity, and individual liberty. And we will begin to see how our narrow focus on the sacredness of earth leads us to discount some of the highest expressions of life, the ones our friends and allies in these other movements care so much about.

Instead of today's mutual denial, where each movement discounts the importance of the other's mission, we need to listen and hear what our adversaries want us to understand. Because until they know that we care, they won't care what we know.

It is only in alliance with them that we will overcome our true adversaries: our institutional selves, the big interests we are all a part of but do not control, and which together smother change; the institutions to whom we granted our power and autonomy, in exchange for industrial era prosperity. There is no need to destroy these institutions—in doing so, we would destroy ourselves. Our opportunity instead is to evolve them into new forms, in which some of the power we placed in them is returned to the individuals and small groups that are the source of our creativity, our resilience, and our sustainability.

We understand that the gloom-and-doom ideology is an effective political organizing tool. When we have run grassroots environmental groups, we tested negative and positive messages against one another. Negative messages that demonized our enemies outperformed positive messages 2.5-to-one. Imminent threats by named villains quintupled the media yielded by a publicity campaign. The activist fundraising marketplace on the right and left literally demands that our adversaries be evil and our challenges overwhelming—or it denies us the capacity to do our work at all.

Battling the demon also made us feel good—it seems to be in our tribal nature to often see only virtue in our community, and only vice in the other. It makes it easier to kill.

But we should not believe our own press releases, fundraising letters, or other tribal calls-to-arms. Nor should we accept that this is the only way we can advance our causes. Even if we cannot let go of the demon entirely, it is important that we substantially narrow our characterizations of it. It is not something immense like "capitalism" or "corporations" or "all progressives" or "all conservatives" or "environmentalists" or "activists." It is, generally, a component of a system that has outlived its usefulness. It does not need to be destroyed. It simply needs to change, and often it will do so as much by choice as by compulsion so that in the end, no one is sure just what led to the change.

So what does this tell us, specifically, about how to protect the climate from imminent collapse, and save humanity from ourselves?

PART TWO: THE AGENDA

What Can We Support Together?

CHAPTER FIVE
KEEP IT IN THE GROUND!
The Unburnable Fuels Scenario

The climate debate is no longer about whether the change is real and human-caused. Even noted skeptical environmentalist Bjorn Lomborg agrees the change is real and we're to blame. Today's skeptics mostly argue that it is a slower-moving phenomenon that we can adapt to with technology.

Technology is key to a solution, but it is no panacea. The rise of atmospheric carbon and related effects will trigger painful discontinuous change. Complacency won't save us. Neither will panic. Resiliency can. That requires something different than militant moderation or evasive action.

Consider the math of climate protection, as explained by Bill McKibben of 350.org, one of the world's most well-known climate campaign leaders:

It's simple math: we can emit 565 more gigatons of carbon dioxide and stay below 2°C of global warming—anything more than that risks catastrophe for life on earth. Burning the fossil fuel that corporations now have in their reserves would result in emitting 2,795 gigatons of carbon dioxide—five times the safe amount.[52]

THE IMPERATIVE:
Stop Fossil Fuels, One-By-One

"Keep it in the ground!" is the rallying cry for environmentalists determined to block extraction, processing, transport, and use of fossil

---

52 350.org. 2019. "Do the Math." Accessed November 7, 2019. https://math.350.org/.

fuels.[53]   The strategy, based on what they call the Unburnable Fuels narrative, has a simple clarity that drives a simple solution: stop burning fossil fuels.[54] Since our movement has failed to pass either a global treaty or U.S. federal legislation that can do so at a large scale, it uses the tools left to it: laws, lawsuits, and market campaigns, mostly in wealthy democracies, where we have a chance for marginal victories.

Here in the U.S., activists are battling the energy sector head-on at the local, state, and federal level, seeking to block every form of fossil fuel, beginning with those that are either most carbon intensive (coal, then high-carbon oil such as from Canadian tar sands or Nicaraguan crude), or politically vulnerable (such as Arctic oil or natural gas from hydraulic fracturing, commonly called "fracking").[55]

To nudge, cajole, or compel business and lawmakers to keep these "unburnable fuels" in the ground, mainstream advocates deploy a combination of legal, policy, and marketplace tactics. EPA regulations limit power plant emissions.[56] Lawsuits seek to block or close coal plants. Market campaigns try to convince companies to shift purchases away from Canadian tar sands. Renewable portfolio standards require electric utilities to favor sources such as wind and solar power.[57] Federal funds and state tax credits encourage broader deployment of renewable energy.

But we know we are in a holding pattern, waiting for better political opportunities to emerge. We understand that even if our current agenda were to be fully adopted in the U.S., it would accomplish little unless China, India, Russia, and much of the rest of the world followed suit. More urgent action is needed, and some leaders are proposing a more comprehensive break from the past.

---

53 KeepItinTheGround.org. 2019 "Over 400 Organizations Call on World Leaders: End New Fossil Fuel Development." Accessed November 7, 2019. http://keepitintheground.org/.

54 Jakob, Michael, and Jérôme Hilaire. 2015. "Climate Science: Unburnable Fossil-Fuel Reserves." Nature 517 (7533): 150.

55 USGS (U.S. Geological Survey). 2019. "What Is Hydraulic Fracturing?" Accessed November 7, 2019. https://www.usgs.gov/faqs/what-hydraulic-fracturing?qt-news_science_products=0#qt-news_science_products.

56 EPA (U.S. Environmental Protection Agency). 2019. "Cleaner Power Plants." Accessed November 7, 2019. https://www.epa.gov/mats/cleaner-power-plants.

57 Ballotpedia. 2019. "Renewable Portfolio Standard." Accessed November 7, 2019. https://ballotpedia.org/Renewable_Portfolio_Standard.

"BREAK EVERY FREE MARKET RULE"

In a major article in The Nation, Naomi Klein, a prominent progressive leader, issued a far-reaching call-to-action. Free market capitalism itself is a core driver of climate change, she asserts. Capitalism itself is the enemy.

To save the planet, Klein says we must "break every rule in the free-market playbook ... with great urgency. We will need to rebuild the public sphere, reverse privatizations, relocalize large parts of economies, scale back overconsumption, bring back long-term planning, heavily regulate and tax corporations, maybe even nationalize some of them, cut military spending and recognize our debts to the global South. Of course, none of this has a hope in hell of happening unless it is accompanied by a massive, broad-based effort to radically reduce the influence that corporations have over the political process. That means, at a minimum, publicly funded elections and stripping corporations of their status as 'people' under the law. In short, climate change supercharges the pre-existing case for virtually every progressive demand on the books, binding them into a coherent agenda based on a clear scientific imperative."

THE HARD PATH TO SUSTAINABILITY

The path that Naomi Klein proposes is a hard one, in many ways. It is a hard sell politically because it requires broad voluntary economic sacrifice, as the affluent world shifts wealth toward developing nations. It is hard economically because it requires major increases in government spending, to pay for revamping the entire industrial infrastructure. It is hard democratically, because it is questionable whether in a democracy people in affluent nations could really be persuaded—even in the absence of corporate political money—to consistently vote to mandate reductions in current economic living standards to apportion more global resources to the developing world, and to spend much of what's left on public works carried out by government. After all, much of the Tea Party and conservative base in the U.S. isn't even convinced climate science is valid at all, and a major leap in government power and spending is not on their current "to do" list. To protect climate, political success on the scale Klein seeks has to happen everywhere—in every U.S. state, in every affluent nation, and every developing one. In practical terms, the change we need is not likely to happen on this path.

This path is also hard philosophically. It appears to take clear steps away from America's legacy of personal economic freedom, and likely challenges our notions of democracy as well. Even with 2014's record-high percentage of U.S. adults identifying as politically liberal, still, less than 25 percent of the public embraces a progressive agenda of the type that she advocates.[58] If over a quarter of the U.S. population doesn't shift suddenly to the left and spontaneously embrace the political and lifestyle changes that Klein believes are essential, the environmental community could be seen as tempted to support authoritarian decision-making processes, where experts make "smart" decisions on behalf of a public they consider to be acting against its own interests, to force the people to do what's right. It is exceedingly unlikely that most environmentalists—including Klein—would actually support such an effort, and even if somehow they were to support it, it would be very unlikely to pass, and if adopted, even less likely to work in the way environmentalists intend.

THE CATASTROPHIST CREED

Driving us down the hard path is the catastrophist creed: the plausible contention that climate change threatens imminent catastrophe. We don't have time for evolutionary "systemic change." The threat demands immediate evasive action. We need a revolution to take down corporatist big oil, now.

---

58 Gallup. 2015. "U.S. Liberals at Record 24%, but Still Trail Conservatives." Gallup, January 9, 2015. http://www.gallup.com/poll/180452/liberals-record-trail-conservatives.aspx.

Oddly, climate denialists tend to take the same position, but on behalf of a mirror-opposite agenda. The progressive threat to freedom and prosperity is imminently catastrophic, they warn. In the guise of climate protection, leftists are destroying the industries that deliver prosperity, and replacing free enterprise with global government planning. We don't have time to gradually convert them. We need to rid the nation of the progressive threat. We need a revolution to take down leftwing statism, now.

In his brave inside-the-tent critique of the catastrophist creed, Climate: A New Story, Charles Eisenstein describes how scientists and writers like Guy McPherson, Paul Ehrlich, Paul Beckwith, David Wallace-Wells, and Malcolm Light criticize "mainstream climate science along many of the same lines as the skeptics do."[59] Like the skeptics, they believe "scientists ignore data that doesn't fit their worldview, or for which they are psychologically unprepared." But unlike the skeptics, they believe imminent catastrophe is the outcome being discounted. Scientists are toning down their forecasts, they say, to avoid appearing shrill and panicky, and losing their influence. Privately, mainstream scientists are much more pessimistic than their public statements indicate, the catastrophists contend. As Eisenstein explains it,

> *The truth, they say, is that we are doomed. Oddly enough, climate skeptics and climate catastrophists come to a similar place of inaction from entirely opposite directions. What does it matter, when one party disengages because they think there is no problem, and the other disengages because they think there's no solution? Apocalyptic thinking in general fosters a complicity with the very systems that it critiques. Seemingly radical, the catastrophist position is in practical terms completely compatible with the continuation of business-as-usual. Making a similar point, the scholar Eileen Crist writes:*
>
> > *Indeed fatalism is a mind-set that strengthens the trends that generate it by fostering compliance to those very trends. The compliance that fatalism effects is invisible to the fatalistic thinker, who does not regard him or herself as a conformist, but simply as a realist.[60]*

59 Eisenstein, Charles. 2018. Climate: A New Story. Berkeley, CA: North Atlantic Books.
60 Crist, Eileen. 2007. "Beyond the Climate Crisis: A Critique of Climate Change Discourse." Telos 141 (Winter): 29-55.

The "realism" upon which so much climate discussion is based takes for granted many of the same beliefs and systems that are generating the crisis to begin with. What we believe to be real, though, may be a projection of the story we live under. As for the systems, humans created all of them. Humans can change all of them. Catastrophist prognostications of doom range from massive disruptions that would render the tropics uninhabitable and devastate food supplies, all the way to near-term extinction of human beings (in my lifetime) or even a runaway greenhouse effect that would make Earth like Venus.

Paradoxically, the catastrophists and denialists each point to legitimate possibilities: that we face potential catastrophe, and the economic or ecological end could be near. The worries that drive the believers also come from a justified sense of unease: Politicians and interest groups aren't putting solutions on the table that match the severity of the crisis. This is true. Oddly, however, those same entrenched interests profit from the division that results when each extreme believes their version of catastrophe is imminent. This distorts the political agenda of both the catastrophists and the denialists, by separating them from one another, and engaging them in war. The production-and-consumption machine hijacks their partial truths and uses them to stoke polarization.[61] That keeps the problem-solving majority—divided into right and left halves—from acting on the sum total of the insights on both ends of the spectrum. The problem is not that the catastrophists and denialists are both mostly wrong. The problem is that they are both partly right, and the machine won't let us deal with the implications of that dual threat. We're forced to choose: increase the power of the state in combination with corporations to save the environment or increase the power of corporations in combination with the state to save the economy.

---

61 Lindsey, Brink. 2008. The Age of Abundance: How Prosperity Transformed America's Politics and Culture. New York: HarperCollins Publishers.

THE CASE OF THE CATASTROPHISTS
From Climate–A New Story, by Charles Eisenstein[a]

I invite the reader to browse Guy McPherson's website, "Nature Bats Last," for a catalog of the scientific evidence behind their position.[b] Basically, near-term extinction depends on positive feedback loops that accelerate climate change. For example: Arctic warming melts undersea methane hydrates, releasing methane into the atmosphere and causing more warming. The same occurs for stores of methane and carbon dioxide in permafrost. Hotter temperatures generate more water vapor, which traps more heat. Arctic ice melt decreases albedo (reflectivity), generating more warming from the sun. Warming causes shifting climatic patterns, leading to forest fires and peat fires, creating soot that dirties the snow, causing faster melting. Methane release from bodies of freshwater increases with higher temperatures. More atmospheric CO_2 leads to more carbonic acid in the rain, which dissolves calcium carbonate rocks, releasing more CO_2 into the air. Most of the alarm centers on methane. According to Malcolm Light, the methane under the Arctic Ocean alone is a hundred times greater than that sufficient to instigate a major extinction event. If even 1 percent is released, it would cause a 10°C rise in global temperature—enough to ensure the demise of all vertebrates.[c] And, say the catastrophists, this is already well under way and irreversible. The feedbacks are already in place. The Arctic will soon be ice-free. The Larsen B and Larsen C ice shelves are on the verge of collapse. The West Antarctic Ice Sheet is losing 150 cubic kilometers of ice per year. The oceans are warming at twice the rate previously thought. Sea level rise has gone exponential. I will not repeat the previous exercise and walk the reader through the mainstream responses to these points, the responses to the responses, and so forth. Methane levels haven't risen as quickly as the catastrophists predict. Yes, they have—the methane has gone to a higher atmospheric layer than where the measurements are taken. No, they haven't—that claim is speculation based on sketchy data. Yes, they have... I seriously recommend the interested reader spend a solid week reading catastrophist literature, and another solid week reading skeptic literature (the website Watts Up With That? is a good place to start, or Matt Ridley's essay "The Climate Wars' Damage to Science").[d] It is amazing how intelligent human beings, all sourcing information from what we call science, can come to such dramatically opposed conclusions. What's going on here? Each camp wields various psychological and political theories to explain the intransigence of the other. Each side is certain that the science is with themselves. For reasons that will become apparent in this book, I do not accept the catastrophist narrative. It does, however, have three important truths to offer. First, a great dying is indeed under way on this planet, and human activity is responsible for it. Most people and institutions have their heads in the sand and do not see it or allow themselves to feel it. Second, we are indeed facing the end of the world. Not the literal end of civilization or the human species, but a transition so profound that on the other side of it, it will seem like we are living in a different world. That is how deep the changes must go for the ecological crisis to be resolved. We face an initiation, a metamorphosis, into a new kind of civilization. From this place, what is possible, practical, and realistic changes as well. Our successful graduation to a new world is by no means guaranteed; nonetheless, the catastrophists are channeling the truth of a possibility. They see the necessity of a death phase, the dying of our present collective self; they do not see the rebirth. And that is normal. In a true initiatory ordeal, often there is a moment when there seems no hope of ever making it through. Third, the catastrophists are right that conventional means, methods, and mindsets are far insufficient to the task of healing the planet. The catastrophists are like the voice that tells the man in the maze, "Just stop." They do not recognize that after this stopping a new compass becomes available, a song that can guide us out. The situation is hopeless, yes—but only from within the logic and worldview that entrap us. That worldview (which has generated the crisis to begin with) renders us impotent, because its solution set is entirely insufficient to the task at hand.

a. Eisenstein, Charles. 2018. Climate: A New Story. Berkeley, CA: North Atlantic Books. pp. 70-74.
b. McPherson, Guy. 2019. "Nature Bats Last." Accessed November 7, 2019. https://guymcpherson.com/.
c. Light, Malcolm. 2014. "Focus on Methane." Arctic News, July 14, 2014.. http://arctic-news.blogspot.com/2014/07/focus-on-methane.html.
d. Ridley, Matt. 2015. "The Climate Wars' Damage to Science." Quadrant Online, June 19. https://quadrant.org.au/magazine/2015/06/climate-wars-done-science/. Perhaps in an effort to establish its credibility, this essay indicts as pseudoscience other deviations from conventional opinion, such as belief in homeopathy or the dangers of genetically modified food.

The simplistic plans that climate catastrophists put forth to avoid climate catastrophe are founded on three errors in thinking that divert them from an authentically sustainable path: Climate Reductionism, Carbon Fundamentalism, and status quo Political Pragmatism.

CLIMATE REDUCTIONISM

Climate Reductionism is reducing the complexity of systemic causes to a simplistic and programmatic one: carbon. Cut carbon out of the economy, reduce our carbon footprint to zero, and all is solved.

With $4 billion in grants promised by 29 foundations[62] to NGOs who fight climate change, the incentive is overwhelming to cast every environmental issue as part of the war to eliminate carbon emissions. Draining wetlands, clear cutting forests, eroding soils, killing fish, poisoning air, damming rivers, killing off predators, disrupting the carbon and water cycles, and degrading ecosystem resiliency in other ways are secondary concerns. Cutting carbon becomes the ultimate catch-all goal.

62 Hewlett Foundation. 2018. "Philanthropic Community Announces $4 Billion Commitment to Combat Climate Change." Press Release, September 14, 2018. https://hewlett.org/newsroom/philanthropic-community-announces-4-billion-commitment-to-combat-climate-change/.

CARBON FUNDAMENTALISM

Climate Reductionism leads straight to Carbon Fundamentalism. There's a simple enemy to defeat: the carbon industry. Big oil, big gas, and big coal. It's a big enemy, to be sure, but an easily-identifiable one. We know how to beat that enemy: mobilize a bigger campaign than they can, and shift more dollars toward the politicians, strategists, and industries that can replace our big enemy with our big friends: big solar, big wind, and big clean tech. Then go on, big business as usual.

STATUS QUO POLITICAL PRAGMATISM

Carbon Fundamentalism then sets us up for Political Pragmatism. Klein's utopia sounds straightforward enough, but it runs up against an unfortunate truth: the political status quo won't replace big institutions with small decentralized ones, clean or otherwise. Politically, there's just too much money to be extracted from big business and big government—even the combined dollars of big foundations and big investors can't outspend the other big spenders. So instead, Congress and the states deliver what politicians call "all of the above." That turns out to be *big everything*. Big nuclear, solar, and wind so we have zero carbon fuel; big gas to lower our carbon footprint, and big carbon capture technologies to clean up the big oil and slightly-less-big coal. All in a politically managed market that has plenty of room to protect every concentrated vested interest, but not the public.

It sounds logical, rational, and compelling to manage the market to sustainability. And don't get us wrong: all these technical fixes are probably part of the solution. But they are far from sufficient. Their fatal flaw is that they lock in the big centralized institutions of our industrial past. They require massive expenditures of public dollars, to subsidize institutions that are too big to innovate, under conditions set by power brokers who profit by selling false promises of change to voters while delivering too much protection against change to the status quo.

If the U.S. were a giant corporate state like China, a managed transition to politically-selected winners might make sense for a generation or so. But then the big institutions would break down. Natural ecosystems are not sustainable because they concentrate power in giant top-down structures; their creativity and resilience comes from processes of feedback-and-adaptation that lead to ever greater diversity, and the creation of new kinds of value, from the ground-up.

No government-centric planning regime can choose winners and losers accurately, year in and year out, for years and generations. Only markets can do that. But as we know, those markets will fail if externalities like pollution and destruction are socialized.

In a sustainable ecosystem, the big create space for the small, the uniform for the diverse, and the established for the novel. All the big corporations that big government will manage to death can also excel in a sustainable economy. Their own survival will depend not on seizing ground from the small and diverse, but by opening niches that allow diversity to flourish. Some enterprises will grow, some will shrink, some will practically disappear as new ones emerge. But this will only happen if the right and left unite behind smart low-cost regulations, including pollution prices, and let the marketplace find the best ways to drive energy efficiency up and carbon, nitrous oxides, sulfur dioxides, and particulates down. Until we build a left-right coalition representing the problem-solving 70%, political strategists and bureaucrats will increasingly manage energy markets to protect the flow of dollars from vested interests to them, locking in the players with the most political power. You know who that is.

The better strategy is to change what is politically possible. That requires shaking up the rigid system that divides the left from the right and puts fundamentalists like Klein in charge of the rhetoric, while keeping policy under the thumb of power brokers who sell it.

The advantage of this approach—besides the fact that it will work—is that it is founded on the very ecological principles that Klein and others want to protect. It takes a systems approach to save our natural systems.

CHAPTER SIX
IT'S NOT ALWAYS HARD BEING GREEN.
A Soft Path to Sustainability

Despite massive growth in the market for wind and solar power, the global share of fossil fuels versus renewables has stayed relatively constant, and carbon emissions hit an all-time high in 2018 and 2019. Perhaps the popular philosopher Kermit the Frog was right when he reportedly said, "It's not easy being green."

But as sources of earth-saving guidance, amphibian hand puppets can be less than reliable. No matter Kermit's counsel, the Hard Path is not the only path to the future—and quite likely, it leads only *away* from sustainable prosperity.

The Hard Path to the future, clean or otherwise, is hard-wired into our production and consumption machine. That's one of the reasons the forced-march approach of fundamentalists right and left have such media appeal. Rational top-down industrial methods of production and consumption are what helped beat the Depression and win the war. The Marshall Plan assisted rebuilding Europe and Japan. The military-industrial complex took us to the moon. So naturally, they are the go-to tools that entrenched institutions favor for dealing with climate change today. Because the left and right are divided, the only climate policies that are politically feasible are those that serve the *production* complex that generates products and services. The messages that keep the public divided are those that serve the *consumption* complex—the corporate and other institutions that manage the media echo chambers to maximize ad sales.

It doesn't matter that the dominant media narratives demonize the entrenched institutions. The left can hate corporations and the right can hate the state all they want. What's important is that they never join forces to challenge the production or consumption complex.

The separation of our left and right halves prevents the creative possibilities unleashed when their thinking is integrated. It's not that every time the left and right engage they generate a breakthrough idea. In fact, most engagements lead nowhere, and most innovations fail. What's destructive is that innovations are never given a chance to be tested. As former NIH director and Nobel laureate Harold Varmus explains, the system now favors those who can guarantee results delivered by entrenched groups rather than potentially path-breaking ideas that, by definition, cannot promise success.[63] Young innovators are discouraged from straying too far from postdoctoral work tightly linked to established developments. Seasoned inventors stick to established paths of innovation rather than exploring new fields. Some climate researchers say they are afraid to publish results that contradict climate orthodoxy because they do not want to be labeled a "denier."[64]

In a highly influential *Foreign Affairs* article in 1976, Lovins coined the term "soft energy path" to describe an alternative future where energy efficiency, smart design, and renewable energy sources would outperform the dominant "hard energy path" dominated by large centralized energy systems, facilities, and institutions.[65]

While not all of his expectations were fully borne out, Lovins' soft path more closely reflects the direction energy development has taken in the years since, than the linear forced-march path projected by mainstream energy analysts at the time.

---

63 Alberts, Bruce, Marc W. Kirschner, Shirley Tilghman, and Harold Varmus. 2014. "Rescuing US Biomedical Research from Its Systemic Flaws." PNAS 111 (16):5773-5777.

64 Eisenstein, Charles. 2018. Climate: A New Story. Berkeley, CA: North Atlantic Books.

65 Amory Lovins. 1976. "Energy Strategy: The Road Not Taken?" Foreign Affairs, October 1976. http://www.foreignaffairs.com/articles/26604/amory-b-lovins/energy-strategy-the-road-not-taken.

Lovins accurately foresaw the dramatically increased role that energy efficiency would play in meeting the nation's energy needs beginning in the 1970s. During that decade, which was marked by two energy crises, the U.S. finally broke the seeming iron law of energy and GDP, which asserted based on 50 years of experience that GDP grows in direct one-to-one proportion to energy consumption.[66] Lovins understood that it was cheaper to save energy than buy it; that while efficiency often required new designs and incentive structures, its underlying cost-effectiveness gave it more intrinsic potential as a major solution to energy demands than big capital intensive initiatives like fossil fuel projects and nuclear facilities, or even wind and solar farms.

As Lovins anticipated, between 1974 and the late 1980s, the largest source of energy for the U.S. economy was what he called "negawatts." Efficiency increased the productivity of each unit of energy by more than 40 percent. By 1988, over 30 percent of the nation's energy needs were provided, in effect, by efficiency, using 1974 as a base.

By efficiency, Lovins wasn't just talking about tightening belts, switching to coffee mugs, or even building more efficient cars, homes, and appliances. A soft energy path, in Lovins' view, represented a fundamental shift from an economy dominated by big centralized institutions driving mass production and consumption, toward one in which not just energy generation, but power in many of its social and political forms, is decentralized across a broader range of people and institutions.

Lovins explained that the most profound difference that distinguishes the soft and hard paths is their different socio-political impact. Both paths result in social change, "but the kinds of social change needed for a hard path are apt to be much less pleasant, less plausible, less compatible with social diversity and personal freedom of choice, and less consistent with traditional values than are the social changes that could make a soft path work."[67]

---

66 Tverberg, Gail. 2015. "Charts Showing the Long-Term GDP-Energy Tie (Part 2—a New Theory of Energy and the Economy)." Our Finite World, February 5, 2015. https://ourfiniteworld.com/2015/02/05/charts-showing-the-long-term-gdp-energy-tie-part-2-a-new-theory-of-energy-and-the-economy/.

67 Lovins, Amory B. 1976. "Energy Strategy: The Road Not Taken?" Foreign Affairs, October 1976. https://www.foreignaffairs.com/articles/united-states/1976-10-01/energy-strategy-road-not-taken.

Hard-path proposals, while intuitively appealing in their linearity, would take us in the opposite direction. They trade away creative market institutions and instead centralize power in government agencies charged with planning, owning, running, or regulating. Theoretically, corporations would adhere tightly to the rules set forth by government. But in practice, that's not usually how it works. Big government and big business on today's scale are both industrial-era institutions, growing off each other so that what benefits one tends to benefit the other.

A soft path, by contrast, is not dependent on extensive social planning, centralized decision-making, and large-scale capital allocation that meet specifications of central authorities. In fact, a major emphasis is to avoid commitments to inflexible infrastructure and centralized institutions that lock society into particular patterns for decades.[68] The soft path relies instead on economic signals that cultivate efficient use of energy, smart design of homes and buildings, diverse energy sources matched in scale and quality to end uses, and special reliance on "soft energy technologies," then thought of as solar, wind, biofuels, hydroelectric, and other renewables.

By staying flexible and adaptive, Lovins contended that a soft path could gently double the efficiency of oil utilization, step-by-step, as individuals freely choose from among a variety of options, from simple basic tools to advanced technologies, lightweight materials, and digital communications.[69]

Soft energy paths focus on meeting needs, not building pipelines and power plants. Lovins reminds us that energy consumption is not an end in itself, but a means to a variety of social ends. We don't want big power plants and high electric costs, he often says, we want hot showers and cold beer.[70]

68 Ibid, 141.
69 Lovins, Amory B., E. Kyle Datta, Odd-Even Bustness, Jonatha G. Koomey, and Nathan J. Glasgow. 2005. Winning the Oil Endgame: Innovation for Profits, Jobs, and Security. Snomass, Colorado: Rocky Mountain Institute.
70 Ward, Logan. 2007. "Amory Lovins: Solving the Energy Crisis (and Bringing Wal-Mart)." Popular Mechanics, October 1, 2007. https://www.popularmechanics.com/science/green-tech/a2146/4224757/.

Delivering what people want is easier if you give them options for how to get it. Top-down decision-making often results in one-size-fits-all solutions, hard-wired because of the money spent to implement them. Decentralized decision-making allows diverse approaches at the local level that meet the preferences of specific individuals and communities.

Hard paths are paved in straight lines based on central plans and institutional controls. Soft paths meander gently from bottom-to-top and side-to-side, reflecting the creative decision making of individuals and small groups in their communities. They reflect the diverse and adaptive character of small-scale free markets and complex natural ecosystems. They embody the natural characteristics of feedback and adaptation, which enable ecosystems to thrive.

The vision that Lovins set forth inspired a generation of activists, who took up the cause in the 1970s by advocating not just renewable energy, but decentralized soft innovations across-the-board. Stewart Brand's *Whole Earth Catalog*, Jerry Brown's Office of Appropriate Technology, magazines like Mother Earth News and Mother Jones, and the early sustainability movement itself all reflected the sensibilities of people grown tired of big centralized institutions, whether corporate or government.[71,72,73,74]

Today, innovators like architect William McDonough, naturalist Janine Benyus, and many others inspire environmental and mainstream followers alike with their vision of a world that uses nature not primarily as a place to extract and dump resources, but as a source of ideas.[75,76]

William McDonough came to public notice in 1984 when he commissioned by Environmental Defense Fund to design their

71 Whole Earth Catalog. 2019. "Exploring Whole Earth." Accessed November 8, 2019. http://www.wholeearth.com/history-whole-earth-catalog.php.
72 Pursell, Carroll. 2007. The Machine in America: A Social History of Technology. Second Edition. Baltimore, MD: The John Hopkins University Press.
73 Mother Earth News. 2019. "Mother Earth News: The Original Guide to Living Wisely." Accessed November 8, 2019. https://www.motherearthnews.com/.
74 Mother Jones. 2019. "Mother Jones." Accessed November 8, 2019. https://www.motherjones.com/.
75 McDonough, William. 2019. "About." Accessed November 8, 2019. https://www.mcdonough.com/.
76 Biomimicry Institute. 2019. :Janine Benyus.: Accessed November 8, 2019. https://biomimicry.org/janine-benyus/.

new headquarters to meet high standards for indoor air quality and environmental sustainability. McDonough embraced the challenge and soon became renowned for his capacity to articulate, define, and deploy on green principles.

He went on to design major sites for The Gap, Nike, Herman Miller, and Ford Motor Company—the latter a 20-year, $2 billion environmental re-engineering of the company's legendary River Rouge Plant in Dearborn, Michigan, which included the world's largest " living roof."

McDonough built his sustainable architecture practice in part by criticizing the concept of sustainability itself. "Who would want simply a *sustainable* marriage," he says often.[77] Is that our highest aspiration—mere survival?

McDonough tells us that environmental problems are fundamentally "design challenges." He frames design as "a beneficial, regenerative force—one that seeks to create ecological footprints to delight in, not lament."[78] He often says his aspiration is to design something like a tree, something that creates good, like oxygen, rather than minimizing negative impact.[79] His designs incorporate multiple connections with nature, "lots of daylight and natural ventilation, roof-mounted PV panels, water cisterns to harvest rainwater, and rain gardens to absorb any storm runoff."[80] They draw on the biophilia hypothesis—the study of the human desire and physiological need for contact with nature.

If McDonough splashed onto the sustainability scene in the 1980s, Janine Benyus seeped in during the late 1990s and has flourished ever since, inspiring followers with her lovely expressions of Biomimicry, the art and science of nature-inspired design. Benyus, a Rutgers-trained naturalist with degrees in natural resource management and English literature, teaches that human beings should consciously emulate nature's genius in our designs.

77 McDonough, William, and Michael Braungart. 2013. The Upcycle: Beyond Sustainability--Designing for Abundance. New York, NY: North Point Press.
78 William McDonough + Partners. 2019. "Design Approach". Accessed November 8, 2019. https://www.mcdonoughpartners.com/design-approach/.
79 McDonough, William. 2005. "Cradle to Cradle Design." TED2005. Video, 19:48. https://www.ted.com/talks/william_mcdonough_on_cradle_to_cradle_design?language=en.
80 McDonough, William. 2009. "Partners Flow House In New Orleans." Inhabitat July 13, 2009. https://inhabitat.com/william-mcdonough-partners-flow-house-in-new-orleans/.

Nature has at least a 3.8 billion year history of product R&D from which we can draw, Benyus and others point out.[81] They cite a host of examples: leaves are advanced solar cells that self-replicate; spiders create web silk as strong as the Kevlar used in bulletproof vests; tiny hooks on the surface of burs inspired the development of Velcro. Termite's ability to maintain constant temperature and humidity in their termite mounds, despite extreme temperatures, led to office buildings that cut energy use 90 percent. Mussels create glues as adhesive than the most advanced invented by humans. Beetles harvest water from fog.[82]

But Lovins, McDonough, Benyus and their colleagues are rediscovering insights that have occurred to humans throughout time, as they learned from the natural forces surrounding them.

One of the early examples of biomimicry was Leonardo da Vinci's "flying machine," which emulated the flight of birds. The Wright Brothers derived inspiration for their first heavier-than-air aircraft from observations of pigeons in flight.[83]

Ancient philosophers the Arabic world noticed that when certain common substances were brought together, they would form uncommon substances with emergent qualities or "spirits."

Alchemists are infamous for trying to discover the formula to turn lead to gold. They never succeeded at that transformation, but along the way, they discovered many combinations that yielded qualities, in many ways, as good as gold.

Modern science itself, in fact, turns the art of alchemy into a more exacting set of disciplines, describing how common substances can be combined to create uncommon ones with emergent qualities. Physics describes how subatomic particles—protons, neutrons, and electrons—when brought together in various combinations, form 118 distinct atomic elements, each with its own unexpected characteristics. Chemistry

81 Biomimicry Institute. 2019. "What Is Biomimicry?" Accessed November 9,. 2019. https://biomimicry.net/what-is-biomimicry/.
82 Biomimicry Institute. 2019. "Biomimicry Examples." Accessed November 9, 2019. http://biomimicry.org/biomimicry-examples/.
83 Howard, Fred 1998. Wilbur and Orville: A Biography of the Wright Brothers. New York: Ballantine Books. p. 33. ISBN 978-0-486-40297-0.

describes how, when these elements are combined in thousands of ways, they form air, water, and myriad of other compounds, with an even greater array of emergent qualities. Biology explains how these compounds, brought together to form cells, create emergent forms of life. Sociology and history and all the social sciences describe how these living beings join together to create complex communities of people and other living things.

In each combination, something is spent, but something different is earned. Each atomic, chemical, biological, and social combination takes energy and resources. But each generates entirely new qualities that are absent in the parts, yet present in the wholes.

This capacity of nature—to "upcycle" a simple set of resources into a more complex whole—is fundamental to sustainability. Life itself is one of these emergent qualities.

Systems Science

Science, biased by industrial thinking, has grown dependent on reductionism. The essence of reductionism is that as we break complex wholes into their parts, and as we move from living systems to their non-living programmed parts, we notice that reality is *reduced.* Our higher qualities disappear one at a time. Like HAL the computer at the end of *2001: A Space Odyssey,* we lose everything that makes life not just worthwhile, but life.

This is what pits science and religion against each other, and contributes to the segregation of religious Americans into the Republican Party, and college-educated voters into the Democratic Party. Scientists have somehow decided that the qualities that emerge when parts come together as wholes don't actually exist. Lacking material form, these qualities, we are told, are imaginary. We aren't conscious. We have no freedom. We don't actually love. We just think we do. Life is an illusion created by chemicals. We are accidental outcomes of random freak interplays of lifeless soulless matter.

Systems science suggests an alternative to the dismal implications of reductionist thinking. In *What We Learned in the Rainforest—Business*

Lessons from Nature, Bill and his coauthor Tachi Kiuchi described the three Laws of System Dynamics that help living systems escape the fate suggested by scientific reductionism.[84] They positioned these three as parallel to the Laws of Thermodynamics, which describe what happens as systems are taken apart.

Today, sustainability is the art and science of smart design—creating structural arrangements that harness system dynamics to yield precise qualities, while minimizing negative side effects. The qualities released through design can be applied in ways that are beneficial or harmful. As we discover ways to unleash new capacities, people and companies gain new power and assume new responsibilities.

Lovins, McDonough, Benyus and their contemporaries have their critics. Some believe they oversell the potential of efficiency, design, biomimicry, and renewables, exaggerating their economic benefits and underplaying technical barriers. Some criticize them for adopting hard-path components to their agendas, seeking to ban or mandate certain technologies, processes, or chemicals, rather than adopting responsibility-based approaches that might achieve better results. Some point out that efficiency alone won't stop overconsumption—unless external costs are internalized, as economists would say, it could simply lead to cheaper products and raise overall depletion.

Nonetheless, updated to reflect today's political and economic environment, these gaps can be closed, and the soft path vision holds a number of key advantages over the hard path model that all of us too often advocate.

First, it is friendlier to things Americans care about—freedom, choice, variety, democracy, community values, and personal responsibility.

Second, it is more aligned with digital technologies, which tend to disrupt big institutions, favor creativity and innovation, and potentially empower people. A soft path wouldn't set the environment against technology—it would favor technologies that put power and choice in the hands of people. And of significant political importance, it would dramatically expand the potential of the digital sector.

---

84 Shireman, Bill, and Tachi Kiuchi. 2002. What We Learned in the Rainforest—Business Lessons from Nature. San Francisco, CA: Berrett-Koehler Publishers, Inc.

Third, it has broader political appeal, attracting free market libertarians, technology entrepreneurs, fiscal conservatives, traditionalist do-it-your-selfers, and small-is-beautiful progressives who think globally but act locally.

Fourth, it is compatible with the principles of sustainability in nature, the processes of feedback-and-adaptation that enable a rainforest to grow diverse, integrated, resilient and sustainable.

Fifth, it is much more likely to actually get the job done. In fact, while it's hard to conceive of exactly what governments could mandate to assure a 350 ppm world with a maximum 2-degree temperature increase (despite their seeming firmness, hard path proposals do not guarantee that outcome), it's far more likely that a soft path open to human creativity and innovation could approach that goal, or even surpass it in time.

Even today, the barriers to a soft energy path are not primarily technical nor economic. They are mainly institutional and include an array of entrenched federal subsidies, innovation-resistant industrial practices, market-limiting regulatory structures, obsolete building codes, poorly-designed utility rates, inappropriate tax incentives, imperfect access to capital markets, and fragmentation of government and corporate responsibilities.[85]

Those industrial-era standards reflect the linear planning world that Lovins sought to overturn in the 1970s. If those institutional barriers could be removed, Lovins wrote in 1977 that a soft energy economy "can be constructed in the United States with straightforward soft technologies that are now demonstrated and now economic or nearly economic."[86]

That hasn't happened yet, but thanks to the disruptive power of digital technologies, innovators and entrepreneurs are beginning to undermine the hard rules of the industrial era, challenging every industrial age monopoly and oligopoly to either establish its dominance through its political influence, or adapt and redefine itself for a new era.

---

85 Lovins, Amory 1977. Soft Energy Paths: Towards a Durable Peace. New York: Harper & Row.p. 35.
86 Ibid, 45.

Yet many of the institutional barriers that Lovins alluded to are still intact. Perhaps it is time for a coalition from the political left to the right to begin to dismantle them.

HARD PATH	QUALITIES OF A SOFT PATH	SOFT PATH
Centralized	**POWER**	Decentralized
Top-Down	**DECISION-MAKING**	Bottom-Up
Mandates *Ban Externalities*	**POLICY TOOLS**	Responsibilities *Internalize Externalities*
Big and Industrial	**SCALE**	Small and Human
Capital Intensive	**KEY RESOURCES**	Design Intensive
Uniform *Competitive*	**CULTURE**	Diverse *Integrated*
Source of raw materials	**NATURE**	Source of innovation and ideas
Machines	**METAPHOR**	Living Systems

CHAPTER SEVEN
THE CLIMATE CHALLENGE

WHAT WE KNOW, AND WHAT WE DON'T KNOW

At EarthX each year, we gather top scientists and engineers from MIT, ExxonMobil, and Greenpeace, among others, to review what most agree we know, with high certainty, about climate change: [87]

First, global warming is real—global temperatures have risen, on average, about 1.4 degrees Fahrenheit (0.8 degrees Celsius) from 1880 to 2018, according to NASA.[88]

Second, rising atmospheric levels of greenhouse gases, notably carbon dioxide, are the primary cause. The carbon dioxide-equivalent composition of the atmosphere has been altered in our lifetimes, and not in a small way. The parts-per-million total increased from about 280 in the late 1700s, to 350 in 1989 (a 25 percent increase in 200 years), and now hovers over 400 (a 15 percent spike in the past 25 years), and will likely reach at least 500 by the year 2050.[89,90]

87 CIRES (Cooperative Institute for Research in Environmental Sciences). "Time History of Atmospheric Carbon Dioxide, by CIRES & NOAA." CIRESvideos, May 2, 2014. Video, 1:31. https://www.youtube.com/watch?v=UatUDnFmNTY.
88 NASA (National Aeronautics and Space Administration). 2019. "Global Temperature." Accessed November 10, 2019. https://climate.nasa.gov/vital-signs/global-temperature/.
89 Lindsey, Rebecca. "Climate Change: Atmospheric Carbon Dioxide." NOAA's ClimateWatch Magazine, September 19, 2019. https://www.climate.gov/news-features/understanding-climate/climate-change-atmospheric-carbon-dioxide.
90 IPCC. 2014. "Summary for Policymakers." In Climate Change 2014: Mitigation of Climate Change. Contribution of Working Group III to the Fifth Assessment Report of the Intergovernmental Panel on Climate Change, edited by Edenhofer, O., R. Pichs-Madruga, Y. Sokona, E. Farahani, S. Kadner, K. Seyboth, A. Adler, I. Baum, S. Brunner, P. Eickemeier, B. Kriemann, J. Savolainen, S. Schlömer, C. von Stechow, T. Zwickel and J.C. Minx. Cambridge, United Kingdom and New York, NY: Cambridge University Press. https://www.ipcc.ch/site/assets/uploads/2018/02/ipcc_wg3_ar5_summary-for-policymakers.pdf.

Third, the greenhouse gas and temperature increases are caused primarily by human activity—cars, power plants, and other mostly industrial activities.[91]

Fourth, the effects will be disruptive, to weather, climate, and the economy, unequally across the globe.[92]

Fifth, at some point, if carbon emissions and resulting global mean temperatures continue to increase, and nothing else kills us first, we would face significant and potentially catastrophic disruptions.[93,94]

Here is what most experts agree we don't know:[95]

First, we don't know how much average global temperatures will rise, in response to any particular increase in carbon composition.

Second, we don't know how disruptive the temperature increases will be, to climate, weather, or the economy, especially at the national or local level. We don't yet which weather systems will be affected, and which will not.

Third, we won't know which greenhouse gas levels are sustainable versus catastrophic until years or decades after the emissions have happened. We may have sealed our fate by the time we know.

In the political process, environmentalists and *reasonable* skeptics of action fill in these gaps with their preferred assumptions: for skeptics, that we should not radically threaten our prosperity today when so many crucial questions still remain unanswered; for environmentalists, that

---

91 The National Academies of Sciences, Engineering, and Medicine. 2019 "Understanding the Climate System." Accessed November 10, 2019. https://sites.nationalacademies.org/sites/climate/SITES_193558.
92 NOAA National Centers for Environmental Information. 2019. "Societal Impacts." Accessed November 10, 2019. https://www.ncdc.noaa.gov/societal-impacts/.
93 Carbon Brief. 2019. "The Impacts of Climate Change at 1.5C, 2C and Beyond." Accessed November 10, 2019. https://interactive.carbonbrief.org/impacts-climate-change-one-point-five-degrees-two-degrees/?utm_source=web&utm_campaign=Redirect#.
94 NASA Global Climate Change. 2019. "The Effects of Climate Change." Accessed November 10, 2019. https://climate.nasa.gov/effects/.
95 Kirtman, B., S.B. Power, J.A. Adedoyin, G.J. Boer, R. Bojariu, I. Camilloni, F.J. Doblas-Reyes, A.M. Fiore, M. Kimoto, G.A. Meehl, M. Prather, A. Sarr, C. Schär, R. Sutton, G.J. van Oldenborgh, G. Vecchi and H.J. Wang. 2013. Near-term Climate Change: Projections and Predictability. In Climate Change 2013: The Physical Science Basis. Contribution of Working Group I to the Fifth Assessment Report of the Intergovernmental Panel on Climate Change, edited by Stocker, T.F., D. Qin, G.-K. Plattner, M. Tignor, S.K. Allen, J. Boschung, A. Nauels, Y. Xia, V. Bex and P.M. Midgley. Cambridge, United Kingdom and New York, NY: Cambridge University Press. https://www.ipcc.ch/site/assets/uploads/2018/02/WG1AR5_Chapter11_FINAL.pdf.

the catastrophic risks associated with these same unknowns demand fast and aggressive action now. To translate this concern into concrete objectives, they advocate a maximum 2-degree Celsius increase in temperatures, which they say is correlated to 450 ppm atmospheric carbon.[96] The science doesn't go this far—but politics makes it necessary to close the gap.

By holding tight to this convenient solution formula, we then need to support a set of policies that would guarantee these results. A less rigid approach is not politically acceptable. At first glance, it makes less intuitive sense. But more pragmatically important, interest groups whose support we need would not have the confidence to make the political and business investments required. Businesses and investors may take risks when they need to, but they prefer guarantees and can spend millions on lobbying and political contributions to secure them.

That is how simple federal legislation—for anything—turns quickly into complex compilations of specifications, formulas, mandates, guarantees, and pork. It is how the proposed Waxman-Markey climate legislation of 2009 evolved into an increasingly complex carbon trading system that could have cost half-a-trillion dollars a year, so that enough money could be passed around to coal companies, engineering companies, labor unions, and clean and renewable technology investors to enable the bill to pass. Even that level of spending wasn't enough to overcome opposition. In the end, mainstream environmentalists went along and supported the legislation, but many privately worried that this "as good as it gets" proposal in practice would actually be a setback for climate.[97]

The strategy might have worked in 2009, at least politically, if President Obama had not already spent much of his political capital to barely pass the Affordable Care Act. But it's not at all clear the environment would have benefited by Waxman-Markey. The hard-path strategy forces us to rely primarily on a set of rent-seekers—specific financial beneficiaries—to

96 Gao, Yun, Xiang Gao, and Xiaohua Zhang. 2017. "The 2 °C Global Temperature Target and the Evolution of the Long-Term Goal of Addressing Climate Change—From the United Nations Framework Convention on Climate Change to the Paris Agreement." Engineering 3 (2): 272-278. https://doi.org/10.1016/J.ENG.2017.01.022.
97 Eric Etheridge. 2009. "Waxman-Markey: As Good As It Gets." The New York Times, June 24, 2009. https://opinionator.blogs.nytimes.com/2009/06/24/waxman-markey-as-good-as-it-gets/.

secure nearly 100 percent of the votes of one political party, and one or two from the other party to close the gap.

The economic costs of securing that kind of political support can be high. In the environmental case, when we seek to pass state or federal legislation, we usually begin with a relatively low-rent support base—environmentalists, donors, and a few "green" business interests representing clean tech and renewable energy, whose appetites are comparatively light. Then we need to win the support of companies that could benefit from the build-out of a low-carbon economy, like industrial, aerospace, and public works contractors. They have big appetites. Then we need to add energy companies advantaged by a conversion away from coal—perhaps those heavily invested in natural gas. Then, because in many states we still face a struggle-to-the-death with coal lobbyists, we need to add special favors and delays that benefit the coal sector to reduce their opposition, and subsidies for control technologies to ease their transition. Then at the federal level, because we still don't have the votes we need, we have to go state-by-state and district-by-district, adding more gifts to secure the district support that lawmakers need to cast their votes our way.

That's how federal climate legislation evolves from driving carbon reductions to providing guaranteed funding for coal, wind *and* solar.

Witnessing a process somewhat like this on behalf of the 2009 federal Waxman-Markley climate bill, Dr. James Hansen, the nation's top climate scientist and a vocal advocate for action, called it "a monstrous absurdity hatched in Washington after energetic insemination by special interests."[98]

In short, our current strategy for federal legislation—like strategies for significant federal legislation on almost anything—is likely to deliver one of two results:

Likely Result #1: Compromise the legislation so severely that we gain a symbolic victory (which we hope will lead to real ones thereafter), yet have no real positive impact on the problem—and sometimes a negative one—with mandates that benefit huge vested interest groups, at equally huge cost. Or:

---

98 Hansen, James. 2009. "G-8 Failure Reflects U.S. Failure on Climate Change." HuffPost Green, August 9, 2009. https://www.huffpost.com/entry/g-8-failure-reflects-us-f_b_228597.

Likely Result #2: Stand firm for strong comprehensive federal legis-lation (or a global treaty), and lose consistently, hoping that citizens will eventually come to their senses, rise up, and overthrow the regime—which may not happen until the crisis is so bad that the suffering is enormous, and the action far too late.

LEFT AND RIGHT OPTIMISM BIAS

It is easy to understand the frustrations of Dr. Hansen and Naomi Klein. U.S. action on climate has had little if any impact on U.S. emissions to date, much less global emissions.[99] But are urgent hard path agendas like those that Naomi Klein proposes justified by the crisis at hand, and will they do the job?

Of course, many of the actions Klein calls for do need to happen, at least in some places, to some extent. We do indeed need to renew crumbling infrastructure, expand transit options, foster local economic growth, cut military spending, limit centralized power, and share prosperity with the global south. The problem is that, in true industrial form, she calls for these things to be mandated by a central power to happen *everywhere*, and then applies very standardized progressive formulas to bring them about, through decisions made by experts, with democratic support, and every community's best interests at heart.

Klein is optimistic that if corporate political power can be controlled, the people will step forward and use the instruments of a genuinely democratic government, to impose on themselves whatever collective actions may be necessary to save the planet and assure peace and justice. Moreover, this assumes the affluent U.S. middle class will sacrifice its own interests, at least to some extent, to assure a fairer distribution of resources to those on the planet who are less materially well off.

The left and right can both be quite optimistic, as well as pessimistic, but about different things. Their perceptions of the world often shape

99 Climate Action Tracker. 2019. "USA." Accessed November 10, 2019. https://climateactiontracker. org/countries/usa/2018-11-29/.

their political positions—sometimes to the detriment of their political success.

For example, where do environmental hard path proponents get the idea that this would all work out according to their plans? It seems more a feeling, an intuition, than a well-considered belief. Since the time of Rousseau, progressives have tended to believe that nature is supportive, and that people are selfless. They believe that society works best if we just leave nature alone, to produce what we need, and if we just leave people alone, in their communities, to distribute it fairly among themselves.

By contrast, since the time of Hobbes, conservatives have tended to believe that nature is threatening, and that people are selfish. They believe that society works best if we use technology to tame nature and free market competition to channel selfishness to serve our needs. Since people are selfish, the best way to support one another is for us to trade freely, without coercion. That way, each trade will reflect the selfish interest of both parties. Both sides will gain.

Now consider the way progressives and conservatives apply these views to facts about climate, and how their views of those facts could be shaped, even manipulated, to advance political ends unrelated to climate.

Progressives trust in nature. Conservatives trust in markets. So when they see the "hockey curve" rise in global temperatures, progressives are likely to see grave danger, and sound the alarms. Conservatives, however, are likely to see progress—the curves reflect the wealth we have created as we gained more control over nature and harnessed it to advance human development. That wealth enables us to adapt.

Of course, these positions are based more on intuitions than conscious thoughtful decisions. Faced with more information in an honest discussion, both progressives and conservatives can broaden their perspectives while staying true to their beliefs. But since their conversations are usually with people who agree with them, the political path of least resistance is often to believe only the information that reinforces the intuition and group belief.

That makes each side vulnerable. Conservatives can easily be convinced that any sincere desire to curb emissions means the end of prosperity. Progressives can be just as easily convinced that every heat wave or weather event is caused by the hockey stick rise in carbon in atmospheric carbon.

Similarly, since progressives trust nature, it's intuitive to them that "natural" forms of energy like solar and wind can provide all the energy we need, right now—were it not for oil companies and their plot to undermine them. And since conservatives trust markets more than nature, it's easy to convince them fossil fuels are proven and reliable, whereas "natural" forms of energy are a waste of money that are just not viable today.

The key to drawing these two groups together is to motivate both progressives and conservatives to *think*, rather than just trust their intuitions. Since they resist this mightily, large-scale political change is most viable if we force the two bases to think, by mobilizing the political center—the 70 percent of Americans who have views that are a mix of left and right. Rather than building our movement on a rigidly progressive base—and thereby mobilizing the conservative base against us—it is important to force a split in both bases, by building from the middle. The only way to split the bases is to demonstrate to each that we understand, support, and are dedicated to what they care about most. That is, *we have to support the genuine objectives of each side more authentically and substantively than their internal manipulators do.*

CHAPTER EIGHT
CLIMATE SCENARIOS

ACT WITH UNCERTAINTY: WHY NOT TO WAIT FOR BETTER CLIMATE MODELS

Given what we know, and what we don't know, the left and right need to make a joint societal decision: when will we join forces to stem the flow of carbon into the atmosphere? Now, soon, later, or never? And what will we do—what path will we follow? A hard path of centralized power and decision-making, or a soft path that places more power in the hands of people at the local level?

To help inform our decision-making, scientists we gather at EarthX have sought to craft mathematical models, to place reasonable boundaries around the intrinsic uncertainties of climate science. Climate models use quantitative methods to simulate the interactions of the atmosphere, oceans, land surface, and ice. They are used for a variety of purposes from study of the dynamics of the climate system to projections of future climate. Most seek to project temperature changes resulting from increases in atmospheric concentrations of carbon and other greenhouse gases.

They do this by calculating incoming energy from the sun, as well as outgoing energy radiating from the earth, based on complex calculations of the planet's capacity to absorb or convert heat. Any imbalance results in a change in temperature.

The Intergovernmental Panel on Climate Change (IPCC) is a scientific body established by the United Nations Environment Programme

(UN Environment) and the World Meteorological Organization to support the main international treaty on climate change, the UN Framework Convention on Climate Change (UNFCCC). The purpose of the UNFCCC is to "stabilize greenhouse gas concentrations [in the atmosphere] at a level that would prevent dangerous anthropogenic (human-induced) interference with the climate system."[100]

The IPCC does not carry out its own original research.[101] Instead, it advises governments on the findings and implications of published literature on climate science from both peer-reviewed and non-peer-reviewed sources. It summarizes the findings of scientists in a series of five Assessment Reports, prepared by teams of relevant researchers selected from government and observer nominations.[102] Drafts of these reports are made available for public review and comment.

The IPCC's first assessment report was prepared in 1990, with a supplementary report following in 1992.[103] A second assessment report, referred to as SAR, was issued in 1995, with a third assessment report (TAR) in 2001, a fourth (AR4) in 2007 and a fifth (AR5) in 2014. The sixth report (AR6) is anticipated to be completed in 2022. A special report, *Global Warming of 1.5°C* was also released in October 2018.[104]

TAR and AR4 summarized their findings by providing a set of six specific baseline scenarios for global warming. The scenarios reflected different projections for whether society's priority would be *economic growth* (group A) or *environmental sustainability* (group B) and for whether the world economy would be characterized more by *globalization*

---

100 United Nations Climate Change. 2019. "What is the United Nations Framework Convention on Climate Change?" Accessed November 10, 2019. https://unfccc.int/process-and-meetings/the-convention/what-is-the-united-nations-framework-convention-on-climate-change.

101 IPCC. 2019. "About the IPCC." Accessed November 10, 2019. https://www.ipcc.ch/about/.

102 IPCC. 2019. "Reports." Accessed November 10, 2019. https://www.ipcc.ch/reports/.

103 Nakicenovic, Nebojsa, and Rob Swart. 2000. "Emissions scenarios. Special report of the Intergovernmental Panel on Climate Change." https://www.ipcc.ch/site/assets/uploads/2018/03/emissions_scenarios-1.pdf.

104 IPCC. 2018. Global Warming of 1.5°C.An IPCC Special Report on the impacts of global warming of 1.5°C above pre-industrial levels and related global greenhouse gas emission pathways, in the context of strengthening the global response to the threat of climate change, sustainable development, and efforts to eradicate poverty [Masson-Delmotte, V., P. Zhai, H.-O. Pörtner, D. Roberts, J. Skea, P.R. Shukla, A. Pirani, W. Moufouma-Okia, C. Péan, R. Pidcock, S. Connors, J.B.R. Matthews, Y. Chen, X. Zhou, M.I. Gomis, E. Lonnoy, T. Maycock, M. Tignor, and T. Waterfield (eds.)].

(subgroup 1) or *regionalization* (subgroup 2).[105] Like all scenarios, these are based on simplistic assumptions which invite endless challenge. The six alternative scenarios are:[106]

GROUP A—FAVORING ECONOMIC GROWTH

A1FI Fossil Fuel Intensive. Convergent culture, favoring economic growth—income and way of life similar across regions. Rapid economic growth, population 9 billion in 2050 and then gradually declines. Quick spread of new and efficient technologies. *A1FI has the highest projected temperature increase of 4.0, with a likely range[107] of 2.4 to 6.4.*

A1B Same as A1FI, but balanced emphasis on all energy sources. *A1B has the fourth lowest (third highest) projected temperature increase of 2.8, with a likely range of 1.7 to 4.4.*

A1T Same as A1FI, but emphasis on non-fossil energy sources. *A1T ties with B1 for the second-lowest projected temperature increase of 2.4, with a likely range of 1.4 to 3.8.*

A2 Independent global cultures, self-reliant nations. Continuously increasing population. Regionally oriented economic development. *A2 has the fifth lowest (second highest) projected temperature increase of 3.4, with a likely range of 2.0 to 5.4.*

105 The AR5 report also created baseline scenarios which cover a wider range than the previous assessments. The differences between AR4 and the AR5 climate projections are mostly due to AR5 including a larger range of assessed emissions. The Representative Concentration Pathways (RCPs) are four possible pathways of greenhouse gas emissions and atmospheric concentration, as well as air pollutant emissions and land use. They represent a range of emissions and include: 1) RCP2.6 A stringent mitigation scenario which is representative of a scenario that aims to keep global warming below 2 degrees C above pre-industrial temperatures; 2) RCP4.5 intermediate scenario; 3) RCP6.0 intermediate scenario; 4) RCP8.5 very high greenhouse gas emissions. For more details see: IPCC. 2014. "Climate Change 2014: Synthesis Report. Contribution of Working Groups I, II and III to the Fifth Assessment Report of the Intergovernmental Panel on Climate Change." [Core Writing Team, R.K. Pachauri and L.A. Meyer (eds.)]. IPCC, Geneva, Switzerland.
106 IPCC. 2007: "Summary for Policymakers." In Climate Change 2007: The Physical Science Basis. Contribution of Working Group I to the Fourth Assessment Report of the Intergovernmental Panel on Climate Change, edited by Solomon, S., D. Qin, M. Manning, Z. Chen, M. Marquis, K.B. Averyt, M.Tignor and H.L. Miller. Cambridge, UK and New York, NY: Cambridge University Press. https://www.ipcc.ch/site/assets/uploads/2018/02/ar4-wg1-spm-1.pdf.
107 "Likely" means greater than 66 percent probability of being correct, based on expert judgment according to: Mastrandrea, M.D., C.B. Field, T.F. Stocker, O. Edenhofer, K.L. Ebi, D.J. Frame, H. Held, E. Kriegler, K.J. Mach, P.R. Matschoss, G.-K. Plattner, G.W. Yohe, and F.W. Zwiers. 2010. "Guidance Note for Lead Authors of the IPCC Fifth Assessment Report on Consistent Treatment of Uncertainties." IPCC Cross-Working Group Meeting on Consistent Treatment of Uncertainties. https://wg1.ipcc.ch/AR6/documents/AR5_Uncertainty_Guidance_Note.pdf.

GROUP B—FAVORING ENVIRONMENTAL PROTECTION

B1 Convergent culture, favoring environmental protection—income and way of life similar across regions. Rapid economic growth as in A1, but with rapid changes towards a service and information economy. Population same as A1: rising to 9 billion in 2050 and then declining. Reduced material intensity, introduction of clean and resource efficient technologies. Emphasis on global solutions to economic, social and environmental stability. *B1 has the lowest projected temperature increase of 1.8, with a likely range of 1.1 to 2.9.*

B2 Independent global cultures, self-reliant nations. Divided, but eco-friendly. Continuously increasing population. Regionally oriented economic development. Continuously increasing population, but at a slower rate than in A2. Emphasis on local rather than global solutions to economic, social and environmental stability. Intermediate levels of economic development. Less rapid and more fragmented technological change than in A1 and B1. *B1 ties with A1T for the second-lowest projected temperature increase of 2.4, with a likely range of 1.4 to 3.8.*

Professor Mort Webster and a team of colleagues at MIT have also prepared an extensive series of scenarios that give insight on how to approach climate change from an economic and policy perspective. They use the scenarios for risk management purposes, rather than as quasi-deterministic predictions of future global temperatures. Findings published in 2011 help show how climate policy can drive the biggest reduction in climate risk at the lowest economic cost.[108]

The MIT models show that the incremental reduction in risk from lower emissions depends on which rigid target we guarantee not to exceed. For the Business-As-Usual scenario, where we seek to guarantee no more than a 6°C rise by 2100, "the leftward shift in the probability distribution of temperature change and the shrinking of the upper tail from even modest reduction may be sufficient to reduce the bulk of that risk. The

108 Webster, Mort, Andrei P. Sokolov, John M. Reilly, Chris E. Forest, Sergey Paltsev, Adam Schlosser, Chien Wang, David Kicklighter, Marcus Sarofim, Jerry Melillo, Ronald G. Prinn, and Henry D. Jacoby. 2011. "Analysis of Climate Policy Targets Under Uncertainty." Climatic Change 112: 569.

gain from further reductions will decrease rapidly once the upper tail of the distribution is already mostly below the target," the scientists write. "In contrast, much lower targets (e.g., 2°C by 2100) require extreme reductions in emissions before the bulk of the temperature change distribution falls below the target.... (O)ne should not assume linear reductions in risk from increasing emissions mitigation."

AR4 GLOBAL WARMING PROJECTIONS

BEST ESTIMATE (°C)	EMISSIONS SCENARIO	"LIKELY" RANGE (°C)
1.8	B1	1.1–2.9
2.4	A1T	1.4–3.8
2.4	B2	1.4–3.8
2.8	A1B	1.7–4.4
3.4	A2	2.0–5.4
4.0	A1FI	2.4–6.4

In other words, it is very cheap to take the actions needed to prevent the "Business As Usual" 6°C mean temperature increase from happening. Achieving results not-to-exceed the 3.5°C to 4.5°C range appear to be cost-effective and readily within reach using current or near-term technology. But it is very expensive to guarantee a not-to-exceed reduction in emissions toward the 2°C level currently on the "Must Do" list of environmentalists, and the "Pretend To Do" list of a number of governments, such as the leaders from the G8 nations, who endorsed the target at a summit in 2009.

There are at least two reasons these reductions look so expensive. The first is obvious and real: you can take the easy and cheap steps first. The harder and more expensive ones—like capturing every ton of carbon emitted from a factory or power plant and sequestering it underground—is not necessary until you seek to move the guarantee from 3°C to 2°C.

The other reason the last reductions look so expensive is because the climate models don't account very well for non-linear innovation. Scientists develop the models based on specific technologies that they believe can be deployed to achieve the desired reductions. They can't responsibly speculate on what creative approaches we might later devise, to live more enjoyable lives generating even less carbon.

Yet we know that innovation will continue, especially under a soft path policy approach that intentionally cultivates it. With God, Steve Jobs, and Buckminster Fuller as my witnesses, I predict that based on my own rigorously casual review of the models, topping out below 2.5°C will turn out to be more viable than any scientist could responsibly extrapolate, relying on known sets of environmental, industrial, and digital technologies, and the lifestyles we have built around them so far. Those technologies will co-adapt in ways we simply cannot predict today. But the ways they (and we) adapt can be influenced by policy. If we follow a soft path, we will probably still be using some fossil fuels a century from now, just like we're burning some wood today. But carbon will be weaned almost entirely from our energy system in that time, and today's energy companies will have found something very different and very profitable to do.

The insight from the MIT studies is that it is very, very expensive to guarantee that a specific carbon or temperature target, such as 2°C, will be achieved without fostering innovation. Making the guarantee requires such specific mandates that the cost of the system grows to the point of political non-viability. It then becomes primarily a rent-seekers opportunity, practically guaranteeing an outcome that accomplishes little. The legislation adopts a much less significant reduction and aims to achieve it with a hard path of guarantees to existing interest groups.

A different strategic path, based more on actually minimizing risk than pretending to guarantee specific reductions, would be easier to pass and more effective from both an environmental and economic perspective. It would also empower a different set of interest groups to make the choices—in particular, *people* rather than big institutions.

CHAPTER NINE

THE INNOVATION
SOLUTION

A SOFT PATH TO A PROSPEROUS
LOW-CARBON FUTURE

We have only one decade left, and it's possible we always will.

When we were ten years old, scientists told us humanity had only ten years to act before environmental catastrophe is unavoidable. When we were 20, we still had only ten years left. At 30, ten years. At 40, 50, and now 60? You guessed it: around ten years.

That's no cause for celebration—one stumble and we may be doomed. But it does suggest that despite our failure to address ecological threats systemically, we somehow keep the end at bay.

One reason is innovation—especially digital innovation. At EarthX, leaders from The Nature Conservancy, AT&T, Rainforest Action Network, Mitsubishi, Resources for the Future, IBM, Ocean Conservancy, Microsoft, Niskanen Center, Oceana, Google, and other environmental and digital economy leaders collaborate to save the world's oceans, forests, and climate.

They are pioneering a new approach to innovation. Yesterday's industrial-age imperative was to build bigger machines that deplete resources faster. Today we need what the digital economy helps provide: smarter machines, institutions, and processes that enable people to create more value and use less energy and resources of all kinds. We need the *net* creation of value, *by* the people, not just *for* the people.

Labor is an example. From 1890 through 2000, the nation's key innovation indicator was labor productivity. We used machines to replace human muscle power, increasing labor productivity at a rate of roughly 3 percent a year. The result was an overall 14-fold gain: by the end of the century the economy generated 14 times as much value for every hour we spent working.

It took a lot of fossil fuel energy to run those labor-saving machines, and the machines in turn accelerated the extraction and consumption of raw materials. But the benefits were substantial. In the past century, industrialism delivered one of the world's greatest historic triumphs: unprecedented material prosperity for more than one in five of the world's inhabitants.

Before World War II, in all prior civilizations and social orders, "the vast bulk of humanity had been preoccupied with responding to basic material needs," writes Brink Lindsey. "Postwar America, however, was different. An extensive and highly complex division of labor unleashed immense productive powers far beyond anything in prior human experience.... Concern with physical survival and security was now banished to the periphery of social life."[109]

In addition to the environmental consequences, there was also a social price to material prosperity. The institutions that ran the machines of industry were huge and centralized. People voluntarily traded some of their independence and autonomy, to secure the freedom and prosperity enabled by our productive capacities. They came to rely on big government, big unions, and big corporations—who themselves also grew increasingly large and interdependent. These institutions all served a needed social role, despite their drawbacks and inefficiencies.

Today, material affluence has spread, especially in Europe, Asia, and the Americas. But almost half the world's population lives on less than $5.50 a day, and 10% of people are living in extreme poverty on less than $1.90 a day facing extreme deprivations.[110] Meanwhile, to support those

109 Lindsey, Brink. 2007. "How Prosperity Made Us More Libertarian." CATO Institute Policy Report, May 1, 2007. https://www.cato.org/policy-report/mayjune-2007/how-prosperity-made-us-more-libertarian.
110 The World Bank. 2018. Poverty and Shared Prosperity 2018: Piecing Together th Poverty Puzzle. Washington, DC: The World Bank.

of us in the affluent world, we have so accelerated the pace of consumption that we are damaging the earth's biosphere, the natural systems on which all life depends. Global climate change is a well-known consequence of overconsumption, but it is only one of many. Deforestation threatens the planet's biodiversity.[111] Ocean acidification could deplete much of the world's sources of protein.[112] Water shortages are beginning to impact even the wealthiest nations.[113]

In addition, the global economy lacks the full complement of industrial-era institutions that helped assure a fair distribution of economic benefits. Large corporate and government institutions continue to play the dominant role, but labor has no truly global institutional form. Indeed, the world's largest capitalist economy is largely reliant on the world's largest authoritarian one, for the workers that engage in production. The U.S. has unofficially subcontracted some manufacturing nations where labor organizing is against the law. Workers enjoy rising levels of pay but often undergo wrenching social dislocations in order to fit into a manufacturing structure largely modeled on 20th century industrialism. They have no means for collective bargaining, hence lack the power to advance their economic position the way American workers could during our manufacturing era.

While the low cost of labor may be slowing the evolution of traditional manufacturing, change is nonetheless spreading through the economy, driven mostly by digital technologies. Not even political gridlock in the U.S. and authoritarian power in China can stop the digital revolution. Increasingly, the Internet and social media are undermining the rigid controls that helped smooth the political and operational rough edges of the industrial system.

The attributes that enable digital technology to end-run centralized controls are what align them so closely to Lovins' vision of soft energy

111 World Wildlife Foundation. 2019. "Deforestation and Forest Degradation." Accessed November 11, 2019. https://www.worldwildlife.org/threats/deforestation-and-forest-degradation.
112 NOAA Fisheries. 2017. "Understanding Ocean Acidification." Accessed November 11, 2019. https://www.fisheries.noaa.gov/insight/understanding-ocean-acidification.
113 Columbia Water Center. "America's Water Stress Index." Columbia University, Earth Institute. Accessed November 11, 2019. http://water.columbia.edu/research-themes/risk-and-financial-instruments/americas-water-stress-index/.

paths. The industrial machine age multiplied human muscle, but put control in the hands of big centralized institutions. Now we are beginning to multiply the human mind, placing capacities back under the control of people. The new engines of prosperity are *thinking* machines that we can hold in our hands—cell phones, microchips, computers, and a myriad knowledge-embedded apps, products, and services. And the new institutions that tap their potential are often not big and centrally controlled. Increasingly, they are small and quick-moving, or big but decentralized, because by empowering people and enabling change, they can prosper more.

Most important from a sustainability perspective, these thinking machines and the networks they enable—such as the nascent "sharing economy"—enable people to raise not just the productivity of their labor, but that of all resources they use: energy, water, land, materials, as well as their hearts and minds.[114]

Highlighting the potential, the World Economic Forum and McKinsey note the "sharing economy is driven by three primary benefits: economic—more efficient and resilient use of financial resources; environmental—more efficient and sustainable use of resources; and communal—deeper social connections among people. All of these are enabled and scaled by technology platforms."[115]

Of course, many people use digital technologies in more impulsive ways, anchored to video games and social media platforms that seem to waste their time. Nonetheless, for those who choose to rediscover their capacity to create, digital technologies give them new space to do so.

That's in part because the core technologies of the information era can drive huge gains in productivity, especially within the economic silos where they originated—gains not of an incremental percent or two, but leapfrog advances that often reached 100 percent, 1000 percent, or more. Along the way, innovations from the microchip to the mobile

---

114 World Economic Forum, McKinsey & Company, and the Ellen MacArthur Foundation. 2014. "Towards the Circular Economy: Accelerating the Scale-Up Across Global Supply Chains." January 2014. Page 24. http://www3.weforum.org/docs/WEF_ENV_TowardsCircularEconomy_Report_2014.pdf.
115 Ibid.

app are imposing a healthy dose of change on the large institutions that dominated the last phase of growth. They have cultivated change, empowered people, and occasionally disrupted whole sectors, as they introduced new and often radically more productive ways to deliver value for people.

These energy productivity gains for specific activities led to overall gains in economic productivity. Yet the gains were limited. We had the capacity to create more value, but our increasingly obsolete fiscal, tax, and monetary policies kept productivity growth well below rates of debt accumulation.

Today, even as energy productivity continues to increase within the information and telecommunications sector, overall productivity growth is being constrained by this framework of policies and institutions designed for another era.

Yet even as digital technologies open new soft paths for sustainable growth, our political institutions continue to spend time and money repaving the hard paths that lies behind us, keeping the road clear for the big industrial-era institutions and interests that hold formal power.

This is one reason that since the 1970s, our economy has forfeited $7 trillion in domestic growth to fund our foreign oil habit. We have transferred over $1.2 trillion to nations that are either unstable or antithetical to our interests. Those dollars financed the Baathist terrorists under Saddam Hussein in Iraq, the radical Mullahs under the Ayatollah in Iran, and of course al-Qaeda.

But recent innovations in energy technology provide an opportunity to break our dependence. But how should we take best advantage of the opportunity they provide?

THE ENERGY PRODUCTIVITY EXPLOSION

Year	The Innovation	Productivity Gain	What It Enabled	What It Disabled
1960	PACKET-SWITCHING in data transmission	1000%	Arpanet	Circuit-switching and PBX for data, later, voice
1969	ARPANET, predecessor of the Internet	300%	Routers, LANs, faster and better university research	
1974	ETHERNET	100,000%	Internet	
1974	NTEL 8080 MICRO-PRO-CESSOR	10,000%	Personal Computer	Mainframe Computer
1975	ALTAIR PERSONAL COMPUTER	100,000%	Apple II	
1977	APPLE II	100%	Internet and, later, VOIP	IBM
1980s	INTERNET	Immeasurable	World Wide Web	Experts and Reference Desks
1993	WWW	Immeasurable	Email	Post Office
1993	AOL EMAIL	Immeasurable	Commerce	Brick-and-Mortar
1995	AMAZON AND E-BAY	Major	Social Media	Print Media
2000s	SKYPE AND VOIP	Major	Free Long Distance and Video Calls	International Long Distance
2000s	BLOGS, FACEBOOK, TWITTER	Major		Privacy and Institutional Power

THE NORTH AMERICAN ENERGY REVOLUTION:
One More Chance

Now, technology leaps in energy production have revolutionized North America's energy situation. Even with the challenges now presented by low oil prices, we ought not to waste this opportunity. If we repeat our prior mistake and squander our newest fossil fuel windfall, then, in the end, our energy revolution could simply drive trillions more dollars into five nations, at our expense: Saudi Arabia, Iraq, Iran, the United Arab Emirates, and Kuwait. That is because, in real terms, these nations are the cheapest sources of oil, albeit by just a few dollars a barrel after the U.S. fracking revolution.[116] So long as global demand is high and oil is strategic, they will exercise a major influence over global markets.

If we can set ourselves free from the constraints of a hard path debt-and-consumption economy, the net effect could be a softer path of development, one more supportive of freedom, choice, innovation, small institutions, and decentralized power.

The real potential for a soft path lies in the shift from an industrial economy *refined* by information, as exemplified by virtual storefronts like Amazon, toward a truly new economy *founded* on it—a place where industry is simply part of a new system that transcends and includes it, just as agriculture is part of the industrial world today. As Henry Jenkins, professor at the University of Southern California, and former director of the Comparative Media Studies Program at MIT, says, "For those of you keeping score, the dotcom era has ended.... We are no longer talking about interactive media technologies; we are talking about *participatory culture.*"[117,118]

---

116 See additional details at: EIA. 2019. "Oil: Crude and Petroleum Products Explained." Accessed November 27, 2019. https://www.eia.gov/energyexplained/oil-and-petroleum-products/where-our-oil-comes-from.php.
Rystad Energy. 2019. "Rystad Energy Ranks the Cheapest Sources of Supply in the Oil Industry." Accessed November 27, 2019. https://www.rystadenergy.com/newsevents/news/press-releases/Rystad-Energy-ranks-the-cheapest-sources-of-supply-in-the-oil-industry-/.
117 Jenkins, Henry. 2006. "My Adventures in Poland (Part One)." Blog, December 14, 2006.
https://henryjenkins.org/blog/2006/12/my_adventures_in_poland_part_o.html
118 Jenkins, Henry. 2007. "USC Annenberg Center Speaker Series: Henry Jenkins." University of Southern California. Video, 1:19:14. http://www.youtube.com/watch?v=ardhuq677cU.

Unfortunately, while the rapid growth of digital products, gadgets, and games suggest that innovation is robust, our rates of underlying value creation are still far below what they need to be, to generate the sustainable prosperity needed to support our existing middle class, much less the billions of others who seek prosperity alongside us.[119] We are adapting around the edges of the debt economy, but not moving to create real net value.

The full benefits of innovation have so far been repressed by a series of policy decisions and, more important, non-decisions, that have locked the economy into a debt-financed consumerist mode, even when we have the capacity to grow much more, and consume much less.

Bottom line, the economy as a whole is not adapting to a post-industrial form fast enough. Old industrial institutions are hanging on to old forms of power well past their prime, protected by political gridlock and subsidized by debt. Today, rates of innovation are less than half what they need to be to pay down our debts and support genuine prosperity. An important indicator is our current rate of energy efficiency gains, which hover around 1 to 1.5 percent per year. We need to double or triple those rates, to bring them up to the level of the 3 percent average labor productivity gains that enabled broad-based prosperity in the 20th century.

---

119 Hutton, Bruce, Dave Cox, J. O'Toole, and D. Mayer. 2010. "Value Creation: The Promise of Sustainable Development." In Good Business: Exercising Effective and Ethical Leadership. 130-144. http://www.enterpriseethics.org/Portals/0/PDFs/good_business_chapter_11.pdf.

CHAPTER TEN
CLEAN CAPITALISM

A BIPARTISAN GREEN DEAL TO DOUBLE THE PACE OF ECO-INNOVATION

Gloom-and-doom environmentalism—our overwhelming focus on the prospect of climate collapse—is now the most powerful agent driving opposition to our movement. It solidifies our base of support, but numbs those in the middle. Most damaging, it builds a countervailing movement of political, religious, fiscal, and free market warriors, who unite in opposition against the warriors on our side. They join in coalition with an array of status quo interests, to close off genuine opportunities for climate protection.

By declaring war on the right half of the political spectrum, we limit the breadth of our support, and are forced to adopt a rent-seeking political strategy, one that sets one group of big government and big corporate interests against another. In this battle between giants, our giants tend to lose. Even when they win, we often lose.

It is time to shift gears, from our dependence on gloom, to a vision of what is possible, desirable, and within reach: a soft path that offers the prospect of innovation and genuine economic growth, that moves beyond our dependence on both big government and big corporate power, and that shifts power in evolutionary fashion from the institutions of our industrial past back to people at the individual, small business, and community level.

Quantitatively, our goal can be to match or beat last century's rate of innovation, with at least a 3 percent average annual gain in energy and resource productivity across-the-board. Creating value through innovation is one of America's most natural skills. Our people have the creativity, enterprise, and technological capacity to do it again, if we aren't held back by the 20th century's entrenched powers.

Last century we drove more than a 14-fold improvement in labor productivity.[120] This century, our people and technologies give us the capacity to improve energy and resource productivity ten-fold, step-by-step and leap-by-leap, at an average rate that equals or exceeds last century's average of 3 percent per year.[121,122,123]

Achieving that objective—driving a 3 percent annual gain in total productivity—would enable us to pay off our economic debts, but also develop technologies that open a path to prosperity for the world's developing nations, all while sustaining energy and water supplies, and reducing U.S carbon and other pollutants by more than 2.2 gigatonnes by 2020—almost double what is required to meet the IPCC's 2020 minimum target of reducing emissions by 25% from 1990 levels.[124] Innovation would enable us to have, do, and be much more, while consuming, polluting, and wasting much less.

---

120 U.S. Bureau of Labor Statistics. 1890 to 1949, from Historical Statistics of the United States, Series D 683-688, "Indexes of Employee Output", 1869 to 1969; 1949 to 1987, http://www.bls.gov/lpc/ "Industry analytical ratios for the manufacturing, all persons" Superseded historical SIC measures for manufacturing, durable manufacturing, and nondurable manufacturing sectors, 1949-2003 ftp://ftp.bls.gov/pub/special.requests/opt/lpr/histmfgsic.zip; 1987 to 2007, from U.S. Bureau of Labor Statistics, http://www.bls.gov/lpc/, Series Id: PRS30006092, 1987 to 2007. Year 1890 set equal to 100. See also Professor Richard D. Wolff http://rdwolff.com/content/keynesian-revival-marxian-critique

121 Manyika, James, David Hunt, Scott Nyquist, Jaana Remes, Vikram Malhotra, Lenny Mendonca, and Byron Auguste. 2011. "Growth and Renewal in the United States: Retooling America's Economic Engine. McKinsey Global Institute, February 2011. https://www.mckinsey.com/featured-insights/americas/growth-and-renewal-in-the-us.

122 World Wildlife Fund and Carbon Disclosure Project. 2013. "The 3% Solution: Driving Profits Through Carbon Reduction." Accessed November 11, 2019. https://c402277.ssl.cf1.rackcdn.com/publications/575/files/original/The_3_Percent_Solution_-_June_10.pdf?1371151781.

123 Dobbs, Richard, Jeremy Oppenheim, Fraser Thompson, Marcel Brinkman, and Marc Zornes. 2011. "Resource Revolution: Meeting the World's Energy, Materials, Food, and Water Needs." McKinsey Global Institute, November 2011. https://www.mckinsey.com/business-functions/sustainability/our-insights/resource-revolution.

124 World Wildlife Fund and Carbon Disclosure Project. 2013. "The 3% Solution: Driving Profits Through Carbon Reduction." Accessed November 11, 2019. https://c402277.ssl.cf1.rackcdn.com/publications/575/files/original/The_3_Percent_Solution_-_June_10.pdf?1371151781.

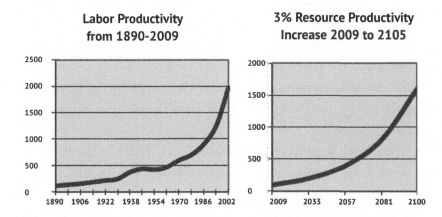

| Labor Productivity from 1890-2009 | 3% Resource Productivity Increase 2009 to 2105 |

This path of innovation plays to our strengths—to the ingenuity of our people, and to the potential of the information-based technologies in which we lead the world.

But neither big government nor big corporations will lead this revolution. We won't find innovation along a hard path dominated by commands-and-controls that lock us into past business models or social roles. Innovation involves the generation of new ideas and knowledge that lead to changes in products, processes, services, organizations, and cultures—and these changes are almost always resisted by status quo interests.

Instead, innovation is most likely to take root on soft ground receptive to the creative capacities of people, and the economic and social entrepreneurism of small institutions. Big business and big government will benefit from the shift, and they too will thrive in the long run, but they will not control the change.

The payoffs are significant. A 3 percent annual improvement in resource productivity can pay down our debts, enable rising prosperity here and abroad, and protect the oceans, forests, and the atmosphere that support life.

If we fail, however, the costs will be heavy. We may set ourselves up for the kind of hard-path non-solutions favored by extremists and ideologues on all sides. We may lurch from one surrender to another—surrendering freedom to impose excessive controls on enterprise, surrendering prosperity to pay off debts too quickly, surrendering the environment to finance one last illusory growth spurt, or surrendering tomorrow to finance business-as-usual today.

To successfully walk the path to innovation, we must break the political gridlock that cements in place the policies of a bygone era, a proud era that has served its purpose. The resource-intensive industrial economy of the last century created unprecedented prosperity. But it also planted the seeds of its successor—an economy that can grow more value with less consumption.

People don't need to be subsidized by government or commanded by corporations to create value. Those capacities lie within them and between them, waiting to be brought to life. All we need do is support the cultivation and development of creative potentials, by nesting them in a framework of laws that reward innovation while assuring that negative externalities are owned, that responsibilities are taken seriously, that we are good stewards. In this way, when people create value, the rewards accrue to themselves, their families, their nation and the world.

The most realistic policy set that cultivates sustainability turns out not to be solely directed to that end. Instead of paving a hard path to that goal, to the detriment of other goals, it is systemic: it simultaneously advances longstanding objectives of conservatives, progressives, free market advocates, religious groups, traditionalists, and small-is-beautiful greens. It doesn't meet their simplistic litmus tests—it forces all of them to embrace their core principles more fully, and to *think* rather than *feel* their way toward their embrace.

One example of such a policy set, which we advance in *Innovation Nation*,[125] would advance a new era of value creation by adopting private and public policies that advance ten principles:

1. **SET A NATIONAL GOAL.** Target a 3% annual gain in overall productivity in public policy, not as a singular mandate, but as a target to guide our progress.
2. **SET SECTOR GOALS.** Leading companies in each sector set their own goals, in consultation with experts and stakeholders, that support 3% national gain.

---

125 Business Roundtable. 2019. "Innovation Nation: An American Innovation Agenda for 2020." Accessed November 11, 2019. https://innovation.businessroundtable.org/.

3. **UNLEASH PEOPLE.** Cut public and private barriers to individual enterprise, especially small business and microenterprise.

4. **CUT AND FIX TAXES.** Stop taxing jobs, income, and prosperity. Cut payroll and income taxes, for both individuals and companies. Remove barriers to clean tech investments. Tax pollution instead, starting with carbon.

5. **WIND DOWN SUBSIDIES.** Stop subsidizing the past—wean us off unnecessary spending that supports obsolete practices in industry and agriculture.

6   **INCREASE RESEARCH.** Fund R&D for the future—especially basic and applied research with broad multi-sector benefits—to drive both incremental and breakthrough resource gains.

7. **PROTECT AIR, WATER, AND LAND.** Reduce environmental and climate risks, and use the market to foster conservation and stewardship, such as through prices on pollution.

8. **RENEW CITIES AND COMMUNITIES.** Reform outdated codes and end barriers to small business, microenterprise, and the sharing economy to revitalize big cities, small towns, and local communities.

9. **REFORM GOVERNANCE.** Move beyond gridlock, toward government that is democratic, accessible, functional, and free.

10. **INCLUDE EVERYONE.** Celebrate the capacities of all people in all their diversity, respecting and welcoming women and men, gay and straight, minorities and majorities to contribute fully, without prejudice.

These ten principles do not need to be applied through a single global treaty or federal omnibus bill. They can weave themselves into and throughout society along ten thousand winding paths, like water finding its own way.

The opportunities for activists, entrepreneurs, artists, creators, and internal corporate and governmental change agents are innumerable, and the multiplier effects from their implementation will accelerate our transit along a path of change. We don't need a desperate lunge for the end zone from the 50-yard line suggested by ideologues. We simply need to spread out across the whole field of play, and do our parts, accumulating millions of incremental gains.

TOWARD A SOFT PATH ALLIANCE TO DOUBLE INNOVATION RATES

Consider again the natural and unnatural alliances that need to be formed in a hard path versus a soft path battle. The hard path pits green environmentalists, solar and wind advocates, and clean tech investors against the U.S. Chamber of Commerce, the National Association of Manufacturers, every major trade association, and advocates of free market capitalism. Major brands, retailers, and digital sector mostly stand on the sidelines officially, because they know if they indicate support, they set themselves up for retribution by one party or the other, for advancing a policy set neither wants to happen.

The formula then that environmentalists need to follow to win the hard path battle is a rent-seekers strategy: guaranteed financial and regulatory benefits to specific engineering projects, control technologies, forms of energy (both black and green) and district-based constituents.[126] The policy tools that deliver those benefits with assurance are primarily mandates. The level at which they must be adopted is federal, and then global.

Status quo interests representing generic "business" have far superior political firepower for this battle, though the public's strong desire to protect health and the environment will bring greater success than raw political power suggests. The likely outcome is tougher but not necessarily better regulations, higher costs and therefore a lower share of the market for coal, and improvements in carbon intensity in the standard 1-1.5 percent annual range. If economic growth exceeds those numbers, then overall carbon emissions will increase, but not as much as the "Business As Usual" model suggests.

---

126 Marotta, David John. 2013. "What Is Rent-Seeking Behavior?" Forbes, February 24, 2013. https://www.forbes.com/sites/davidmarotta/2013/02/24/what-is-rent-seeking-behavior/#60cd8c6e658a.

The outcome we can expect: Very high economic costs, in return for insignificant U.S. emissions reductions, and on a global level, an IPCC-projected temperature increase of 2.4 to 3.4 degrees Celsius, but possibly as high as 5.4 degrees. Little if any better, in other words, than if we had passed no environmental legislation, and saved our money.

The soft path strategy pits green environmentalists, digital technologies, and competitive clean tech and renewable technologies against status quo business and labor interests. Genuine free market advocates would either sit on the sidelines out of cultural aversion or distrust of the environmentalists, or if they were rational, they would side with the soft green path, because it favors small and competitive enterprise, rational markets, and low tax rates. Coal would remain in strong opposition; Big Oil is already marginally supportive[127]; gas would benefit, but some of the sector's leaders simply distrust and despise environmentalists, so the sector would be divided.

Critically, major consumer brands and retailers would be in play. Temperamentally, they prefer to stay out of these battles—their lobbyists are embarrassed by open displays of public spiritedness by their employers. It's so naïve and *soft*, so rookie league, to actually care about something in the cynical Washington beltway. They like to conform to group norms, and save their political chits for special favors, like everyone else on K Street. But the brand owners and marketers know that both their sales and their reputations would benefit from the soft path, which puts more money in consumer pockets and frees up money that would otherwise be spent on taxes or energy. A little pressure from the public, and the consumer brand and retail leaders would need to offer their support, or suffer reputation damage and local policies they would dislike. With the support of one or two senior executives who actually care would come political support from a vast array of small and regional enterprises, who depend on the brands for their business.

---

127 For example, ExxonMobil publicly supports a revenue-neutral carbon tax: "It is rare that a business lends its support to new taxes. But in this case, given the risk-management challenges we face and the policy alternatives under consideration, it is our judgment that a carbon tax is a preferred course of public policy action" (Wilkinson, Carlton. 2014. "Carbon Tax Could Boost Economy as it Aids Global Warming Fight." The Street, May 31, 2014. https://www.thestreet.com/story/12728015/1/why-a-carbon-tax-could-profit-us-business-consumers.html). In addition, ExxonMobil, ConocoPhillips, Chevron, BP and Shell are "planning their future growth on the expectation that the government will force them to pay a price for carbon." (Davenport, Coral. 2013. "Large Companies Prepare to Pay Price on Carbon." The New York Times, December, 5 2013).

CHAPTER ELEVEN

A REPUBLICAN AGENDA
FOR CLIMATE

SOLAR, WIND, CLEANER FOSSIL FUELS,
AND INNOVATION—PLUS TAX CUTS
AND A PRICE ON POLLUTION

Abraham Lincoln opened the national parks. Teddy Roosevelt established the national forests. Richard Nixon signed into law the Clean Air and National Environmental Policy Acts and formed the Environmental Protection Agency. President Reagan negotiated the Montreal Protocol, the most successful environmental agreement in history, the one that drove a global solution to ozone depletion.[128] Democrats may often be first to identify the problems we face, but Republicans are often the first with solutions that work.

One solution that works particularly well is putting a price on pollution. When it's free to pollute, people and businesses tend to pollute freely. When we charge for pollution, we find ways to stop. Both of us have successfully championed the price-on-pollution idea for more than 30 years, in California, Texas, and nationally. In California, this meant breaking a longstanding deadlock between business and environmental interests and establishing a five-cent deposit on beverage containers.

It is extraordinary how much pollution can be cut with a simple financial incentive. California's so-called "bottle bill" cut the state's litter

---

128 UN Environment. 2019. "The Montreal Protocol." Accessed November 12, 2019. https://www.unenvironment.org/ozonaction/who-we-are/about-montreal-protocol.

volume by more than half, and built a recycling industry that still achieves recovery rates of 80%—the highest of any state in the nation except Michigan, where the deposit is ten-cents.[129,130]

But California's system is unique in another respect: it is the lowest cost law of its kind, anywhere. Its low cost can be traced to the fact that it was designed by a coalition that stretched from the political left to right, and included business, environmental, and social justice leaders—back when we were allowed, at least occasionally, to fraternize.

Bill Coors of Coors Brewing Company—the more environmentally concerned of the "Coors Brothers" who progressives often demonized back then—came up with a streamlined structure for the law that cut its cost by more than 90%. Chuck Collings, a social and religious conservative who headed the state's retailers, provided the moral underpinning that motivated for-profit companies to set aside their do-nothing tendencies and take action for the good of the state. Democratic Assemblyman Burt Margolin navigated the measure through the State Assembly, while Republican Senator Becky Morgan steered it through the State Senate. The state's manufacturing interests lobbied Republicans to vote for it, while local beer distributors brought Democrats aboard. It was signed into law by a conservative Republican governor, George Deukmejian, who administered it through his Department of Conservation. The system paid for its own administration, entirely by self-generated recycling revenues and unredeemed deposits, with no funds from the general fund. In the years since, the program has been so cost-effective that the state often raids the recycling fund when it runs short of cash for normal operations. Fortunately, the state's politicians have always paid back the fund, at least so far.[131]

What dismays us is that cynical political strategists have now turned environmental protection into a wedge issue, using it strategically to

129 Container Recycling Institute. 2019. "Bottle Bill Resource Guide: California."Accessed November 12, 2019. http://www.bottlebill.org/index.php/current-and-proposed-laws/usa/california.
130 Container Recycling Institute. 2016. "Michigan Bottle Deposit Information." November 12, 2019. http://www.bottlebill.org/resources/pubs/2016RRMichigan.
131 2009. November 10 Lucas, Greg. 2009. "Major Recycler Sues Over Beverage Container Fund Insolvency." California's Capitol, November 10, 2009. http://www.bottlebill.org/news/articles/2009/CA-11-10-MajorRecyclerSues.htm.

divide people and politicians into groups of homogeneous Republicans on one side, and homogeneous Democrats on the other. If the California recycling law were to be proposed today, representatives from the two parties would not be allowed to bring their best ideas together, to protect the environment without breaking the bank. Instead, Democrats would be expected to vote for the measure no matter how costly it was, and Republicans would be compelled to vote against it no matter how necessary it was. The passion of Democrats to deal with the problem could not be combined with the ingenuity of Republicans to get it done in a cost-effective manner that is good for the economy.

"Wedge issues" are issues selected by political strategists as devices to keep voters segregated into separate media echo chambers. Today's top four wedge issues—abortion, guns, immigration, and climate—will never be resolved until they cease to serve their cynical purpose in political campaigns. They're simply too valuable as agents to divide people into assigned parties and positions. They keep voters from straying into unfamiliar ideological territories where their hearts and minds might be up for grabs.

For Republicans like us today, it is almost a social demerit if we express an interest in protecting the environment in unmixed company. We are regarded as potential traitors to the cause of free markets. It's not that we and our Republican friends want to destroy the environment. We've just been taught to dismiss environmental concerns as either insignificant, or outright hoaxes designed solely to enrich liberal vested interests.

On the other hand, for our Democratic friends today, it is equally unacceptable to express the idea that climate change is anything less than a global emergency requiring the mobilization of government on the scale of World War II, to take evasive action. And guess what—the evasive action would need to be carried out by vested interests Democrats could depend on to line up the votes they would need to govern.

This is how the fear of vested interest control becomes a self-fulfilling prophecy.[132] If zero Republicans are allowed to vote to protect the

---

132 Moe, Terry M. 2019. "Power, Vested Interests, and the Politics of Institutional Reform." In The Politics of Institutional Reform: Katrina, Education, and the Second Face of Power. Pp 10-40. Stanford University, California: Cambridge University Press.

environment, then Democrats often have no choice but to sell out to vested interests capable of lining up the votes they need to pass environmental laws.

If Republicans and Democrats didn't join forces to make recycling work in California, the state would probably still have a recycling law by now. But you can bet it would be channeling money straight to vested interests—politically powerful waste haulers, labor unions, and manufacturers who would be recycling a fraction of what the state collects today, for several times the cost. When protecting the earth—or doing anything else worthwhile—is left to only one political party, vested interests hold all the power. The people hold none.

Why? Because it is practically impossible to line up every vote of every Democrat or Republican for anything. Party line votes invariably require generous political payoffs, generally to vested interests inside specific legislative districts, who provide the campaign support the local lawmaker needs to take a risky vote.

That is not acceptable—not for environmental policymaking, or any policymaking. We need to stop it.

To do that given today's politics of climate, Republicans need to face up to three realities. First, climate change is real and it's largely human-caused.[133] Beyond that, there is much uncertainty in climate science, and room for inquisitive skepticism. But those basics we must accept.

Second, we Republicans pay a huge political and policy cost when we fail to show up on this issue. When we leave climate protection to the Democrats, we ourselves lock them into a political dynamic that requires them to simultaneously cater to the extreme anti-capitalist impulses at the left edge of their progressive wing—who lay 100% of the blame on big corporations and feel government-run industry would do better—and to the vested interests who insist on profiting from the laws that are allowed to pass. In the process, we Republicans lose the votes of women, young people, and many in the religious community, who believe we have abandoned the planet for the sake of profit.

133 The National Academies of Sciences, Engineering, and Medicine. 2019 "Understanding the Climate System." Accessed November 10, 2019. https://sites.nationalacademies.org/sites/climate/SITES_193558.

Third, we need to remember something we have been taught to forget: that there are Republican-friendly, market-friendly, freedom-friendly climate solutions that we can support. Those solutions are more effective than the false big government panaceas Democrats tend to offer. We should be out there, offering our solutions to voters.

Let's dive deeper into each of those three realities.

On climate science, there are three things that we know with a high degree of certainty, and three things that we don't know with certainty. First, global warming is happening. Data from NASA shows conclusively that over the last century or so global temperatures have risen about 1 degree Celsius, most of that increase since 1970.[134] It's around a degree and a half Fahrenheit. We know that in the United States temperatures have increased about 1.3 to 1.9 degrees Fahrenheit since 1895.[135] We know that 2014 to 2018 have been the hottest years in the modern record.[136] We know that the year 2016 was the hottest year on record.[137] We know that today there are more record hot and record cold days than there have ever been before as long as records have been taken. We know that the ratio of hot to cold days is increasing, that it used to be that when we had records we had about half and half record hots for every cold day but now we have about 2/3 of the record temperature days are hot and about one-third of them are cold. So we can surmise that climate is becoming a bit unstable. Temperatures are pushing in the upward direction. Things are getting hotter. But climate is also becoming less predictable. It's not a good thing when the ecosystems that support us become unstable. That is a source of risk that we ought to take seriously.

The second thing we know is that humans are the primary cause of this shift.[138] Greenhouse gas emissions correlate more closely than any other

134 NASA. 2019. "Global Temperature." Accessed November 12, 2019. https://climate.nasa.gov/vital-signs/global-temperature/.
135 National Climate Assessment. "U.S. Global Change Research Program. Recent U.S. Temperature. 2014. Trends." Accessed November 12, 2019. https://nca2014.globalchange.gov/report/our-changing-climate/recent-us-temperature-trends.
136 NASA. 2019. "2018 Fourth Warmest Year in Continued Warming Trend, According to NASA, NOAA." Accessed November 20, 2019. https://climate.nasa.gov/news/2841/2018-fourth-warmest-year-in-continued-warming-trend-according-to-nasa-noaa/.
137 NASA. 2019. "Global Temperature." Accessed November 12, 2019. https://climate.nasa.gov/vital-signs/global-temperature/.
138 National Academies of Sciences, Engineering, and Medicine. 2019. "Based on Science: Humans

theoretical cause to the actual experience of global warming.[139] Green-house gases come from cars, power plants, and industrialized systems of agriculture. And that that's what tightly explains most effectively the rising temperatures. Our friend Dr. Richard Muller, the emeritus professor of physics from UC Berkeley, used to fashion himself at climate skeptic.[140] He is therefore someone we trust on this. He and his colleagues have done extensive studies paralleling many others and they found that compared with alternative explanations—solar flares, natural weather patterns, geological activity and so on—it is the emissions of carbon dioxide and greenhouse gases in the industrial era that most tightly and cleanly correlate to those temperature increases. Before the industrial era, the atmosphere had about 280 parts per million of carbon.[141] By 1989 that had increased to about 350 parts per million, in 2015 it passed 400 parts per million, in 2016 402 parts per million, in 2017 406 parts per million, this year 410 to 412 parts per million, so very clearly the proportions are increasing and it looks like they could reach as much as 500 parts per million by 2050.[142,143] Do we really want to play with this significant a shift in the proportion of carbon in the atmosphere—especially if turning it around could take decades?

The third thing that we know is that the effects of an atmosphere high in carbon will be disruptive to weather, to climate, and to the economy, unequally across the globe.[144] These effects will vary by time and location in unpredictable ways. And if we don't stabilize emissions in the relatively

Are Causing Global Warming." Accessed November 12, 2019. https://sites.nationalacademies.org/BasedOnScience/climate-change-humans-are-causing-global-warming/.
139 EPA. 2019. "Sources of Greenhouse Gas Emissions." Accessed November 12, 2019. https://www.epa.gov/ghgemissions/sources-greenhouse-gas-emissions.
140 Morellow, Lauren. 2012. "Converted Contrarian Argues Humans "Almost Entirely" to Blame for Climate Change." ClimateWire, July 30, 2012. https://www.scientificamerican.com/article/converted-contrarian-argues-humans-to-blame-for-climate-change/.
141 NASA. 2011. "Global Mean CO2 Mixing Ratios (ppm): Observations." Accessed November 12, 2019. https://data.giss.nasa.gov/modelforce/ghgases/Fig1A.ext.txt.
142 NASA Global Climate Change. 2019. "Carbon Dioxide." Accessed November 12, 2019. https://climate.nasa.gov/vital-signs/carbon-dioxide/
143 Jones, Nicola. 2017. "How the World Passed a Carbon Threshold and Why It Matters." Yale Environment 360, Yale School of Forestry and Environmental Studies. Accessed November 12, 2019. https://e360.yale.edu/features/how-the-world-passed-a-carbon-threshold-400ppm-and-why-it-matters.
144 NOAA National Centers for Environmental Information. 2019. "Societal Impacts." Accessed November 10, 2019. https://www.ncdc.noaa.gov/societal-impacts/.

near future it is certainly possible that the consequences will be serious, and possibly disastrous. Those are the three things we know.

Here is some of what we don't know.[145] First, we don't know what temperature change to expect per unit of atmospheric carbon present in the atmosphere. We can't say with any certainty that 350 or 450 parts per million is safe or unsafe, and we can't predict what temperature rise or weather complications will result.[146] Second, we don't know how disruptive these increases will be. We don't know if impacts will follow a linear path, or if there will be thresholds at which impacts either stabilize or destabilize the system. Third, we don't know when we will find the answer to these questions, but we do know it will take decades to learn the answers.

How are the political right and left responding to this uncertainty? The hard-core left, probably provoked by media and organizing imperatives, projects certainty and panic in its response. Activists are certain that 350 ppm is the maximum carbon level we can sustain.[147] And they are panicked that a 1.5 or 2 degree C temperature rise is the most we can survive without catastrophe.[148] The science can't answer those questions, but activists can. We understand why. They fear the worst. But we worry that panic is not a helpful response. It can lead us to make mistakes that are disastrous in even shorter order.

What is the political right's response? The hard-core conservative base is just as extreme as the left's base, but in the opposite direction. We

145 Kirtman, B., S.B. Power, J.A. Adedoyin, G.J. Boer, R. Bojariu, I. Camilloni, F.J. Doblas-Reyes, A.M. Fiore, M. Kimoto, G.A. Meehl, M. Prather, A. Sarr, C. Schär, R. Sutton, G.J. van Oldenborgh, G. Vecchi and H.J. Wang. 2013. Near-term Climate Change: Projections and Predictability. In Climate Change 2013: The Physical Science Basis. Contribution of Working Group I to the Fifth Assessment Report of the Intergovernmental Panel on Climate Change, edited by Stocker, T.F., D. Qin, G.-K. Plattner, M. Tignor, S.K. Allen, J. Boschung, A. Nauels, Y. Xia, V. Bex and P.M. Midgley. Cambridge, United Kingdom and New York, NY: Cambridge University Press. https://www.ipcc.ch/site/assets/uploads/2018/02/WG1AR5_Chapter11_FINAL.pdf.
146 Bruhwiler, L., A. M. Michalak, R. Birdsey, J. B. Fisher, R. A. Houghton, D. N. Huntzinger, and J. B. Miller, 2018. "Chapter 1: Overview of the Global Carbon Cycle." In Second State of the Carbon Cycle Report (SOCCR2): A Sustained Assessment Report, edited by Cavallaro, N., G. Shrestha, R. Birdsey, M. A. Mayes, R. G. Najjar, S. C. Reed, P. Romero-Lankao, and Z. Zhu. U.S. Global Change Research Program, Washington, DC. https://carbon2018.globalchange.gov/downloads/SOCCR2_Ch1_Overview_Global_Carbon_Cycle.pdf.
147 350.org. 2019. "History." Accessed November 12, 2019. https://350.org/about/.
148 Lederer, Edith M. 2019. "UN Climate Chief Warns Current Path Leads to 'Catastrophe.'" AP News, April 25, 2019. https://apnews.com/a0baaad17de744ca875711d92e173442.

project certainty that there's nothing to worry about. We express panic that by proposing action, we will unleash a wave of government actions that will wipe out freedom and prosperity. That turns out to be almost a self-fulfilling prophecy: by failing to put sensible solutions on the table, we ensure that anti-capitalist extremism is taken seriously.

We also look like we are rolling the dice on humanity's future. Polls demonstrate that while climate is not the most urgent priority of voters,[149] it turns more voters away from the Republican Party than abortion, guns, immigration or any of 20 issues. It signals to women, young, and many Christian voters that Republicans are detached from reality, and can't be trusted on any issue. Millions of women and young people—even those who lean conservative—won't even consider voting Republican if they believe we can't accept what we learn from science. Ideological opposition to climate action is self-destructive for Republicans.

Without our ideas, the policy instruments left on the table are the most damaging to freedom and prosperity. We practically guarantee what we call a "hard path" response to climate change, where we declare war against fossil fuels and mobilize government and big corporate and labor interests to eliminate them.

Many progressive activists think the path to the future requires banning fossil fuels and mobilizing a complete shift to solar, wind, and other renewables. That won't happen—it's the kind of absolutist agenda that simply can't be implemented in the real world. But here's what probably will happen, if activists flank the mainstream with campaigns for a 100% conversion. First, we will impose costly and punitive regulations that go well beyond what's necessary to protect the public's health. These regulations will be intended to increase the cost of fossil fuels to make them less competitive with renewables. The effect will be like a price on carbon, but where the money goes to institutions that provide unnecessary control equipment, processes, consulting, reporting, and legal and judicial processes. Second, we will not just encourage renewables,

149 Jones, Bradley. 2019. "Republicans and Democrats Have Grown Further Apart on What the Nation's Top Priorities Should Be." Pew Research Center, February 5 2019. https://www.pewresearch. org/fact-tank/2019/02/05/republicans-and-democrats-have-grown-further-apart-on-what-the-nations-top-priorities-should-be/.

but mandate them, then subsidize them. The effect will be like a partial back-door ban of fossil fuels. Third, we will impose legal and regulatory barriers to the extraction and transportation of fossil fuels at every turn, so that production shifts from inside to outside U.S. borders, mostly to undemocratic nations where fossil fuels flow without environmental controls.

How can we blame the environmental community for following that path, if it is the only one available to them?

It is suicidal not to take our seat at the table and press for a better alternative. But what would be the elements of a conservative approach to clean energy and climate protection?

Pro-Renewables. First, it would start with strong advocacy of renewables. Conservatives in every poll show a great enthusiasm for solar energy and wind energy.[150] Our support makes common sense: for more than a century, the economy has systematically followed a path away from dirtier high-carbon fuels, toward cleaner lower carbon ones. We can champion renewables without falling into the trap of mandating them. We can support research, development, and deployment. We can remove undue regulatory barriers. And we can support benchmarks, if we like, with goals and timelines for driving down carbon and other pollutants.

Pro-Nuclear. We can remove barriers to nuclear energy, one of the few low-carbon sources of electricity.[151] Many environmental leaders have reversed their historic positions on nuclear power, convinced by climate scientists that the technology is far safer than relying on fossil fuels.[152]

Pro-Natural Gas, with methane reductions. Natural gas has been the nation's biggest boon to low-carbon growth. The vast increase in the use of natural gas has squeezed coal out of electricity production, much more than environmental regulations and lawsuits have. We can

150 Ohio Conservative Energy Forum. 2019." Statewide Poll of Conservative Voters Shows Overwhelming Support for Clean Energy Policies." PRNewswire, February 13, 2019. https://www.prnewswire.com/news-releases/statewide-poll-of-conservative-voters-shows-overwhelming-support-for-clean-energy-policies-300795236.html.
151 EIA (US Energy Information Administration). 2019. "Nuclear Explained." Accessed November 12, 2019. https://www.eia.gov/energyexplained/nuclear/nuclear-power-and-the-environment.php.
152 Harder, Amy. 2016. "Environmental Groups Change Tune on Nuclear Power." The Wall Street Journal, June 16, 2016. https://www.wsj.com/articles/environmental-groups-change-tune-on-nuclear-power-1466100644.

multiply the benefits by supporting flex-fuel policies for automobiles, so consumers can easily switch to gas-powered vehicles. But if we support natural gas, we need to support smart regulations to reduce methane leaks from gas extraction, transportation, and use. The point of the regulations would not be to impose expensive mandates and foster lawsuits. They would be to reward performance, by making it more profitable to plug leaks and keep gas from escaping.

Pro-carbon capture and storage. Technologies enable us to capture carbon emissions from coal, gas, and oil, and store them in natural or artificial sinks.[153] Carbon capture can be very expensive, but costs are declining quickly.[154] Once companies can profit from carbon capture, they will provide the political support needed to expand it.

Pro-energy innovation. New energy technologies show great promise. We can't know whether algae-based oils, hydrogen-based electricity, digital efficiency or any of dozens of other alternatives will prove most valuable. Perhaps many will. But we can help environmentalists learn how smart tax, regulatory, and R&D policies can uncover clean alternatives.

Pro-agriculture innovation. Farmers and ranchers are among the original conservationists. They know that today's agricultural practices need to be updated. Farming and ranching has a huge carbon footprint, but it doesn't need to. Agriculture is about growing plants. Plants consume carbon dioxide. As we improve our systems of agriculture through innovation, we are turning agriculture into a net environmental positive, a means to draw carbon out of the atmosphere as we grow the food we need. Our young farmers and ranchers are showing the way.

Pro-Innovation. Above all, Republicans should be pro-innovation. Not just energy or agricultural innovation—we need to support innovation across-the-board. Innovation has proven to be the most

---

153 Varanasi, Anuradha. 2019. "You Asked: Does Carbon Capture Technology Actually Work?" State of the Planet, Earth Institute, Columbia University, September 27, 2019. https://blogs.ei.columbia.edu/2019/09/27/carbon-capture-technology/.
154 Hanley, Steve. 2018. "Cost Of Carbon Capture Plummets Thanks To Two New Techniques. CleanTechnica, December 4, 2018. https://cleantechnica.com/2018/12/04/cost-of-carbon-capture-plummets-thanks-to-two-new-techniques/.

powerful agent for reducing negative impacts of carbon emissions. Many people argue that we need a miraculous new energy source that is both cheaper than fossil fuels and radically lower in carbon emissions. But we don't need to invent that new energy technology. We have it already. The digital technologies that Americans invented, first in Silicon Valley and now in tech hubs all across the country, are radically reducing the effective cost of energy, along with our carbon footprint.

For example, traditional industrial technologies—those reliant on the extraction and use of fossil fuels—can improve energy efficiency about two or three percent per year, with effort. Digital technologies, however—those that rely on information inscribed digitally on microchips—can achieve resource productivity leaps a hundred times those of industrial practices alone. Most microchips are made of the most abundant material on the planet: silica—essentially, sand. By inscribing on silica a design, we are able to embed intelligence within every product and service. The result is that rather than products becoming bigger and more consumptive, digital technologies make them smaller and smarter.

We already have the technologies to radically reduce the amount of energy we need and the amount of carbon we emit. Many of these technologies were born right here in the U.S. The left doesn't understand the role that innovation plays as well as the right does. Republicans can champion innovation, as the best path to a low-carbon economy.

Mathematically the challenge of overcoming the climate problem crisis is not as difficult as it may at first seem. The impulse of the left when dealing with an issue like this is to declare an emergency and mandate a solution. Some progressives call fossil fuel companies criminals, equating them with tobacco companies. This makes it easier to justify eliminating the industry from the planet. But fossil fuels are not like tobacco. They have been enormously helpful in creating prosperity. The question is not how to eliminate them. It is how to improve our resource productivity—to gain more value from every unit of fuel we use. If we can use the technologies of the digital economy to grow resource productivity 3 to 5% here and around the world, we can drive carbon emissions down

80% here and globally within about 50 years. That's what most scientists estimate is needed to bring us into balance.

In short, we have most of the technologies we need to protect our air and climate. We have the innovative capacity to do even more. What we need is the political will to take sensible action. Above all, we need Republicans to come to the table and forge a coalition with Democrats to meet the challenge in a way that protects and enhances freedom and prosperity.

One of the most helpful components of this may be to update the way we tax. In the industrial era, we have taxed prosperity as a fair way to provide government with the money it needs to provide services and infrastructure. But why have we chosen to tax prosperity? Why do we tax profits, income, and sales—examples of prosperity that we want more of? When we tax prosperity, we discourage economic growth.

A Republican approach to climate is a smart Republican approach to economic growth as well. It is smarter to tax things we don't want. Tax air pollutants—like carbon dioxide, nitrous oxides, and sulfur dioxide. Tax emissions of chemicals into water and soil. Tax externalities that subsidize pollution and waste.

For example, Republicans could eliminate two of the most anti-growth and anti-jobs taxes on the books. We could eliminate the remaining corporate income tax, our most anti-growth tax. We could also eliminate the employee portion of the side payroll tax. We could replace these two taxes with an $85 a ton tax on carbon, or an equivalent on other air pollutants. A carbon price of $85 a ton is equivalent to approximately $0.75 per gallon of gasoline.[155] Gasoline prices can shift that much within almost every presidential administration. The economy is well equipped to adapt.

Beyond promoting clean prosperity, the biggest advantage is a continuous drive toward lower taxes. Average per capita income almost always goes up from one year to the next. So when we tax incomes, we

155 Hafstead, Marc and Picciano, Paul. 2017. "Calculating Various Fuel Prices under a Carbon Tax." Resources, Resources for the Future, November 28, 2017. https://www.resourcesmag.org/common-re-sources/calculating-various-fuel-prices-under-a-carbon-tax/.

effectively raise taxes every year. But pollution rates decline each year, especially when they are taxed. If we had an economy that taxed pollution rather than prosperity, we could reduce taxes consistently, year after year. We could cut taxes and carbon emissions by 2-5% each year. What better way to satisfy both conservative and progressive priorities at once?

One of our favorite "clean capitalists" is Rod Richardson.[156] Rod's father helped fund and drive the Reagan Revolution, by developing a series of proposals to reduce the size and cost of government. Now, as President of the Grace Richardson Fund, Rod is bringing bipartisan working groups of economists, scientists, donors, experts, and activists to EarthX, to drive "Clean Tax Cuts."[157]

Clean Tax Cuts (CTC) seek to remove barriers to capital and participation in clean solutions, to reduce waste and negative externalities from modern industrial economies, and accelerate a transition to clean prosperity.

We first met Rod in June 2016, when he joined us at American Renewable Energy Day (AREDAY), a meeting of renewable energy technology and policy, in Aspen, Colorado.[158] His ideas generated so much buzz that we joined him to help launch more than a dozen planning "charrettes"—collaborative, expert-level design sessions—to develop the ideas for application at the local, state, federal, and multi-national level.[159]

CTC aim to accelerate profitable solutions to any kind of waste or pollution, by applying the supply-side principle "if you want more of something, tax it less." In particular, CTCs cut tax rates investors pay on debt and equity in clean investments—these include simple rate cuts to income, dividend, interest, capital gains, and other capital taxes,

---

156 Clean Capitalist Leadership Council. 2019. "BIO: Rod Richardson." Accessed November 13, 2019. https://cleancapitalistleadershipcouncil.org/bio-rod-richardson/.
157 Clean Tax Cuts. 2019. "Clean Tax Cuts (CTC)." Accessed November 13, 2019. https://cleantax-cuts.org/.
158 American Renewable Energy Institute (AREI). 2019. "About AREDAY." Accessed November 13, 2019. https://www.areday.net/areday-2/about-areday/.
159 he Grace Richardson Fund Rocky Mountain Institute & the Sabin Center for Climate Change Law. 2016. "GRF Report on the Clean Tax Cuts Working Group Charrette." Columbia University, September 23 2016. https://cleantaxcuts.org/wp-content/uploads/2016/10/grf-charrette-re-port-161029.pdf.

specifically for investments that reduce the most costly waste and inefficiency—the root cause of all major pollution and negative externalities.

By simply reducing investment tax rates, CTCs remove barriers to capital, which simultaneously increases supply and demand for clean solutions: this one policy both increases ROI and capital investment flows, and reduces cost of capital and cost of outputs. The result? Lots more good stuff, like cheaper clean energy or other waste-reducing solutions. Also, depending on the scope of implementation, millions, perhaps billions, more people participating, investing, living sustainably and working profitably in the fast-growing clean capitalist marketplace and economy.

It is time for Republicans to step forward with environmental solutions. The party needs it. The nation needs it. The world needs it. If we fail, then we lock ourselves into a process of both economic and environmental decline. If we succeed, we demonstrate that we can solve problems Democrats can only complain about. And we might even save the world. Let's step up.

PART THREE:

THE STRATEGY

How Do We Win
This Together?

CHAPTER TWELVE

TEN MISTAKES OF THE
WAR ON CLIMATE
CHANGE

LESSONS FOR WISE CLIMATE FUNDERS, STRATEGISTS, AND ACTIVISTS

"The peak efficiency of knowledge and strategy is
to make conflict unnecessary."
"He will win who knows when to fight and
when not to fight."
– SUN TZU

'The war on climate change—pitting progressives against conservatives—pays off quite nicely for the entrenched Democratic and Republican establishments who make the armaments and soldier the battlefields. Political donors gain from rules and contracts adjusted in their favor. Strategists exploit the war to keep voters segregated for easy management. Lobbyists assure that no left-right alliance can force change on their most reluctant clients. And the thousands of vested interests that pay the political industry for protection keep the status quo in place.

In the process, conservatives, progressives, and the principles they stand for all lose. Strident advocates of the left and right grow increasingly furious that the changes they demand are never delivered. On the left, they attack big money corporatism, and grow increasingly enamored of authoritarian leaders who promise to force their objectives into law. On the right, they decry deep state conspiracies, and grow enamored with authoritarians who pledge to clean up the swamp.

Meanwhile, conservatives who cherish tradition, conservation, and prosperity, and progressives who desire societal change, preservation of nature, and liberation of people, never realize how their destinies are linked.

War may seem essential when an enemy threatens nature herself. Corporations can be cast as the enemy, with fossil fuel companies are their ringleaders. But so can government. So can consumers. So can we all. We all exploit the fossil fuel economy for our own selfish benefit.

There's a faster and easier path beyond fossil fuels, however, and it's one we can help people and companies choose, if we select our tactics wisely.

Here in summary form are ten mistakes that climate funders and strategists should avoid, if their priority is to save a planet, not lose a war.

MISTAKE #1: SELLING CATASTROPHE

It seems to work every time. Catastrophes blamed on evil villains generate 2.5 times the money and 5 times the media, compared with narratives of hope and optimism. But these benefits come with hidden costs:

Catastrophism exhausts our support base. It numbs the public to our calls-to-arms. It alienates those concerned but not alarmed.

A Better Way: Cultivate hope and optimism. Optimism does not raise as much money or media, but it rejuvenates and broadens our base. And new methods of digital outreach can multiply the power of optimistic problem-solvers, as we will explain.

MISTAKE #2: DEMONIZING TOO MANY ENEMIES

Demonization builds opposition to our proposals. Every dollar devoted to demonization generates an opposition dollar. The more demons we target, the more enemies we attract.

Corporate leaders are trapped in the debt-and-consumption machine, just as much as you and I are. They exploit it, as do we, and they profit more than most of us. But they can't change it alone.

A Better Way: The enemy isn't corporations, capitalism, government, or consumers. The enemy is the entrenched system that drives overproduction and overconsumption. We're all part of that system. Engage stakeholders across the system to work together to change it.

MISTAKE #3: SPEAKING ONLY TO THE LEFT

The right and left are natural partners. Their differences are real, but resolvable - and often complementary.

Trying to persuade conservatives to adopt progressive points of view is often futile.

A Better Way: Speak with conservatives in their own language. Understand their worldview. Respect their desire to protect what we have. Develop policy options that reflect their priorities.

MISTAKE #4: DISMISSING CONSERVATION AND STEWARDSHIP

The left, believing that people are selfless and nature is supportive, tends toward a *preservationist* agenda that treats humans as invaders of nature. Hunters, fishers, farmers, and ranchers are enemies of nature, from this point of view.

The right, believing that people are selfish and nature poses risks, tends toward a *conservationist* agenda that treats humans as stewards of the land. Hunters, fishers, farmers, and ranchers are good stewards who love the land, and know it more intimately than most coastal progressives. They are the overlooked half of the environmental movement.

A Better Way: Celebrate hunters, and fishers. Learn how many farmers and ranchers are shifting to regenerative agriculture. Their forebears fed ours for millennia. Invite them to be central players in reducing damage to nature.

MISTAKE #5: CONDEMNING CLIMATE DENIAL

The right and left are being artificially divided because it's profitable for the media and political industries. The fear and hate they are generating is extreme. We feed into it, when we focus on fear, and drive hatred of our adversaries, even those who deny climate change.

A Better Way: The best remedy for climate denial is respect for conservative principles, and acknowledgement that overconsumption threatens both our ecological and economic foundations. Denial will dissipate when our solutions are economically sustainable.

MISTAKE #6: ALIGNING TIGHTLY WITH DEMOCRATS

Over 70% of the public is with us. Aligning with either party turns our majority into a minority. It makes victory impossible.

Any cause or community dependent on just one party is a slave to that party.

The Democratic Party will delay effective climate action until after the next election.

There is always a next election.

The only way to win is with a bipartisan coalition.

A Better Way: Grow an authentic bipartisan coalition where conservatives are free to advance their ideas for meeting the climate crisis, without sacrificing the economy. Challenge conservative donors to join the cause, and match their commitments to climate actions that respect conservative principles.

MISTAKE #7: OPPOSING CORPORATISM WITH STATISM

Big corporations have too much concentrated power. Agreed. The federal government does too. Corporations and governments grow together. Conveniently, the establishment left fights corporate power by building government power, while the right fights government power by expanding corporate power.

A Better Way: Use markets before mandates. Support effective corporate campaigns. Mobilize activists and consumers to avoid companies that aren't part of the solution. Reward companies that are. Above all, use prices to prevent pollution. Support revenue-neutral carbon prices.

MISTAKE #8: JUST BUYING ACCESS AND INFLUENCE

It's tempting to play the inside game, and buy access and influence so politicians will vote for clean energy. Some of this will likely be necessary. But too much can backfire in two ways:

First, the cost of democracy will rise. When clean energy bids up the cost of access, their competitors can match their bids. The result is a more expensive stalemate.

Second, the inside game is rigged in favor of the entrenched. It's not just the fossil fuel sector that's opposing change. It's hundreds of powerful players, and the political pros who take their money. They can overwhelm any team we field.

Our democracy is rigged to resist change, not encourage it. Buying access can protect past gains, but it can't win many new ones.

A Better Way: End-run the insiders. Invade from two directions at once. Organize the left and right together.

MISTAKE #9: SUING THE BASTARDS

Fossil fuels aren't like tobacco. They helped build the industrial economy, overcome the Depression, and defeat fascism. They spawned the technologies that can gradually replace them.

Suing the tobacco industry didn't destroy tobacco. It simply drove the industry into less democratic nations.

It feels good to sue the bastards. But it just creates more bastards.

A Better Way: Stop creating bastards. Challenge fossil fuel companies to put real resources behind their commitments—lobbying resources that can shift the Republican Party's position on climate, and compel Democrats to collaborate on real solutions.

MISTAKE #10: DECLARING WAR ON CLIMATE CHANGE

War is supposed to be the last resort. But we've made it the first.

War is built into our political genes. Whenever we're serious about attacking a problem, we declare war on it. We've declared Wars on Poverty, Cancer, Drugs, Terror, and Hunger. Now we've launched a War on Climate Change.

Wars are profitable for media and campaign strategists, the warriors and weapons makers of the political industry. But they rarely solve problems. And the war to save climate is doing just the opposite. It is exhausting our base, discouraging new recruits, and increasing the size and power of opposing armies.

Climate change is not a challenge that can be won by war. Its systemic cause is an economy and culture addicted to overconsumption. The remedy is the very *opposite* of war. We need to come together to create, not destroy.

A Better Way: Stop the war. Start creating. Engage capitalists, activists, conservatives, progressives, and libertarians. Explore solutions that apply the best ideas from all of them. End-run the debt-and-consumption machine. Create evolutionary change.

You can start by joining us at EarthX in Dallas, to create and celebrate change together.

CHAPTER 13
THE STRATEGY

FIVE MILLION VOTES CAN RECLAIM DEMOCRACY AND SAVE THE PLANET

None of the bipartisan policy solutions we suggest are worth formulating unless we climb out of our ivory tower think tanks and grow the community to make them real. Neither party establishment will let that happen until enough Republican and Democratic *voters* step up and make them an offer they can't refuse.

Let's review the barriers in our way. The current political business model exploits climate change and other wedge issues to lock in the power of what business leader Katherine Gehl and Harvard professor Michael Porter call the Duopoly—the combined Republican and Democratic political, media, fundraising, and lobbying establishment.[160]

The Duopoly maintains its power by isolating voters into two separate echo chambers. A conservative narrative with nationalist overtones draws voters to the right, and a progressive narrative with socialist overtones draws voters to the left. Major media like Fox News and the Wall Street Journal on the right, and MSNBC and the New York Times on the left, have learned to organize content around these two markets, because it drives ad sales.

---

160 Gehl, Katherine M., and Michael E. Porter. 2020. The Politics Industry. Harvard Business Review Press.

The Duopoly further divides voters by identity grievances, exploiting race, gender, ethnicity, and culture to drive us apart, then link our identities to wedge issues that excite our passions—climate, immigration, guns, and most divisive of all, abortion.

Once we're sufficiently riled up, the Duopoly micro-targets us via YouTube, Facebook, Google, and other digital channels. It would be confusing if we began to hate *ourselves* as a result of their messages, so they are careful to point us toward "others" we can fear, exploiting just the right tribal impulses and group prejudices to most efficiently drive voters into either the left-wing or right-wing echo chamber. That keeps citizens from different racial, ethnic, and gender profiles from joining hands to form a governing—good news for professionals who know *much more* about good policy and how to undermine it than the rest of us.

Through these divide-and-conquer tactics, the political media effectively disenfranchises millions of us, which leads to policy gridlock, which locks in status quo interest groups, who grow dependent on political operatives to protect them from us—or them—which allows the two-party establishments to extract duopoly profits, or worse.

We and our friends have obsessed for close to ten years and burned through almost $100 million to figure a way to either overthrow or end-run the duopoly and pass bipartisan legislation to save the planet. Finally, our methods are paying off—we know how to do it. But we need you and a few million friends to help.

The secret plan we've developed—which we're sharing just with you—is to disrupt the Duopoly with an alternative political media business model that destroys the political advantages of fear and hate, gives problem-solvers a 20-point advantage over polarizers, and makes climate denial *politically* suicidal not just for Democrats but also for Republicans—and not just in general elections but primaries as well.

We have taken our plan for repeated test drives, and it has proven its political horsepower in six California races and three state ballot measures. Twenty percent of previously partisan voters vote against polarizers and for problem-solvers, or for reforms opposed by vested interests, even if it means crossing party lines to do so.

The bottom line for us has been two political breakthroughs in the state: democracy reform and climate protection. We passed three California ballot measures to re-enfranchise the majority of voters: redistricting reform, top-two primaries, and transparency rules for state lawmakers. And we elected the pro-environment Republicans whose votes renewed the cap-and-trade climate program first established by Governor Arnold Schwarzennegger. Without them, legislative leaders would have been forced to hand out more public money to secure the final votes they needed.

So what? So that's extraordinary. Most competitive elections these days are won by a percent or two. Presidential contests are decided by exhaust fumes. Our partners have learned how to completely upend that. We can break open the echo chambers, liberate the Solution Citizens from both sides, and help them mobilize as one, in numbers that could decide *every* competitive race in the country, and reclaim an America that both the Tea Party and the Resistance could love. *That's* what.

With quality candidates who refuse to demonize and polarize—candidates dedicated to solutions—we can beat the spread, win back Congress, and occupy the White House by public invitation. Our victory would *not* be one party beating the other. It would be *two* parties competing and collaborating to solve a problem because doing so is in their national and partisan interest. By recruiting just five million Solutions Voters across the partisan divide, we can shift the electoral advantage from extremists of either party to problem-solvers with bipartisan support, at the local, state, and federal level.

The UC Berkeley-educated political scholars, computer modelers, survey researchers, and message-testers who developed the predictive model are fairly bright. The campaign strategists who proved it in practice are skilled practitioners. But it was by liberating voters trapped by the Duopoly that we began to win. Our next steps together are to:

Stop polarizers from winning primaries so voters have quality choices every November.

Undermine identity politics by attracting red *and* blue, women *and* men, younger *and* older, and a full range of America's diversity to problem-solver candidates.

Disrupt vested interest divide-and-conquer strategies with bipartisan problem-solving, that assures a broad governing majority with both **power and purpose.**

Now comes the exciting part: the campaign plan. Before diving into the details, go replenish your caffeine. You might need chemical reinforcement to stay alert, but your democracy, and Mother Earth, will thank you.

THE DONOR ROUNDTABLE PLAN:
Five Million Americans Can Disrupt the Duopoly and Save the Planet

As this book was going to press, with the fiftieth Earth Day just days away, COVID-19 changed everything.

It wasn't the virus itself that knocked the planet sideways. It was the meaning. It meant we weren't safe. We were in danger. Something was coming for us, Asia, to Europe, and then across the ocean for America.

Before COVID, polls showed that for the first time climate could tip the electoral balance. To fully leverage the opportunity, around 40 foundations and families have committed at least $17 billion to save the planet's oceans, forests, and climate, including $4 billion in multi-year funding for clean energy and climate initiatives by 29 foundations, and $10 billion by Amazon founder Jeff Bezos, all beginning in 2020.[161] Other donors have set aside over $1 billion for coordinated ocean and plastics campaigns, and several billion more for independent climate campaigns.

---

161 Hewlett Foundation. 2018. "Philanthropic Community Announces $4 Billion Commitment to Combat Climate Change." Press Release, September 14, 2018. https://hewlett.org/newsroom/philan-thropic-community-announces-4-billion-commitment-to-combat-climate-change/.

The donors are right in their timing, but handicapped in their execution. Their theory of change is incomplete. To press toward the finish line, they are making deep investments on the political left, and strategic ones on the political right. Their better strategy—the one that can deliver transformative change that's healthy for the environment and economy—is a third approach that plays the other two against each other.

Let us explain. Donors are mostly choosing between two paths to change: one fundamentalist, the other pragmatic. Fundamentalist donors are going all-out for progressive Democratic victory. For them, climate is part of a more encompassing social justice movement that confronts capitalism itself, and no compromise with *liberal* Democrats or *any* Republicans will do. Pragmatic donors are following a very different strategy: talk the progressive talk, but walk the establishment walk. To harness progressive energy and keep their activists inside the tent, they adopt progressive rhetoric. To win a legislative majority, they invest deeply in the Democratic establishment, adding just enough strategic Republican assets to eke out a legislative majority.

This poll-messaged numbers-driven strategy often works. It helped pass clean electricity mandates in 29 states where public utilities, corporate leaders, and clean tech investors could often formulate a deal, and grassroots conservatives and progressives could give lawmakers cover. But it falls far short of the systemic transformation needed, for two reasons we can discuss here, and others we can't.

First, politics-by-numbers requires too much policy compromise. To win House support for cap-and-trade in 2009, for example, Congressmen Waxman and Markey handed out so many favors to coal and other interests that Dr. James Hansen and other top climate scientists considered their bill a trillion-dollar step backwards.[162] Paying the tolls required for a partisan climate bill might generate a symbolic victory, but it will be complex, expensive, and deeply compromised.

But there's a second reason that mobilizing an angry progressive base behind an inside political game won't work: the climate war is too profitable

162 James Hansen. "G-8 Failure Reflects U.S. Failure on Climate Change." HuffPost Green. August 9, 2009. https://www.huffpost.com/entry/g-8-failure-reflects-us-f_b_228597.

to end. The battles are already accelerating the political arms race. Every billion tossed by one side into the fire triggers more by the other, generating more heat than light, and even *more* opposition to authentic climate solutions.

To the political media industry, the billions spent to fight climate change are *de facto* contributions to a Democratic Party "attack on capitalism." Power brokers don't even need to point out the threat to their benefactors: industry trade groups and their lobbyists step up for a counterattack. Environmental donors then counter the counterattack, leveraging the outrage of their captive progressive base while investing in a status quo compromise that pays vested interests to solve the problem. We don't blame them. Our future is at stake. But besides the likelihood of backfire, the inside-outside approach is too slow given the crisis we face. It means genuine reductions in carbon footprint will take much longer, cost much more, and require deep and unnecessary economic sacrifice.

Many environmental donors know we need a third leg to this stool. In whispered conversations on the side and hastily-organized lunch meetings, we worry that today's paint-by-numbers strategy is backfiring in three ways:

1. The anti-capitalist rhetoric is narrowing our citizen base, turning off many of the 70% who don't resonate with it.
2. The crisis fundamentalism, even if well-founded, is exhausting our supporters, who fall into denial or despair.
3. The "war on climate change" is triggering billions of opposition dollars to "fight socialism" and any green deal.

There is a way to change the game, but it requires a third type of political investment. We need a political Uber, a well-capitalized upstart to disrupt the Republican and Democratic duopoly that profits from the war on climate change.

We know that the business model of the political media duopoly is to sell political stability, managed change, and consumer demand to the entrenched interest groups of the New Deal era and their latter-day progeny. The deals are sealed from atop two metaphorical towers located in Washington D.C., red and blue edifices with field offices in most state and national capitals. Inside the red tower—let's label it REPUBLICAN LLC—money is extracted from producers of financial, industrial, military, and security goods and services, in exchange for policy stability and managed change. Inside the blue tower, DEMOCRATIC LLC, money is extracted from producers of labor, government, and health and welfare products and services.

The most valuable assets contained at the base of each twin tower are two massive pipelines, one flowing from the offices of their clients to them, the other from the government to them, then continuing on to their clients. Inside each tower, the first pipeline extracts money *from* the holdings of the institutional clients and delivers it *to* the political professionals working in the towers. The second pipeline extracts money, power, and protection *from* the holdings of the nation and people, and delivers it to the professionals and on to the client institutions, to compensate them for their political investments and any policy changes they've agreed to back. The more money the clients pay, and the more change they agree to accept, the more money flows back to them from government, taxpayers, and America's creditors around the world.

Protection from change is not in the near-term best interests of the clients. The New Deal is long gone. Their healthiest course is to adapt to change gradually as it comes. Otherwise, bubbles will burst, systems will fall, and change will be catastrophic. But the political media doesn't sell adaptive change. It's just not profitable enough. The only products they offer are No Change or Managed Change. No Change keeps the rules as they are. Managed Change compensates entrenched interest groups to provide health, military, consumer, or environmental benefits the public wants, using public dollars and debts to pay for them.

When environmental donors invest in the twin political towers, they are caught in the trap. To keep the status quo intact, entrenched interests need only buy into one set of pipelines. Industrial, military, and retirement interests buy red, while labor, health, and welfare interests buy blue. Disruptors who want to unseat the entrenched—like clean energy and environmental donors—must invest in both. Furthermore, to win favors, their investments need to be larger and more reliable than those of the entrenched. No matter how many old money trust funds they tap, they just can't spend enough to buy real change from the establishment. Their only path to victory is to pay entrenched interest groups on both sides to protect climate without altering their power relationships with one another. Hence we can win clean electricity standards that fit an old utility model, or put a price on carbon to pay off the affected interest groups. But we can't pass a revenue-neutral carbon price that cuts taxes to people, raises worker pay, and drives down carbon footprint through efficiency and innovation. The adaptive change of authentic transformation is off the table when the political industry calls the shots.

Every established institution knows which set of pipelines is *theirs*, the one they depend on for protection. If you or I run a successful company, union, or association and want to keep what we have, we need to invest in our side's pipelines. That requires a retainer with a contract lobbyist, who is also a consolidator of political contributions, and partners with a polling, marketing, and communications firm—or perhaps owns one in-house. When threats or opportunities arise, our retained professionals alert us. To protect what we have, they direct us to invest in strategic lawmakers, races, and PACs. Then they consolidate our dollars with others and deliver them in tranches to PACs, 501c4s, 501c6s and campaign committees, so candidates remember who they work for. From there, our dollars are disbursed to pollsters, marketers, communicators, campaigners, and media. The operatives provide most of these services in-house or through close partners, and get a 15% kickback for their media buys.

"Money is the mother's milk of politics," California power-broker Jess Unruh famously said. "Milker bills" are a favorite means of suckling.[163] Most bills introduced in Congress start out as milker bills, toxic to selected interest groups, and nourishing to others. Some are "double-milker bills"—poisonous to two entrenched interest groups at once.[164] Lobbyists detects the toxins, notify their clients, and formulate

163 WiseGeek. 2019. "What is A Milker Bill?" Accessed November 18, 2019. https://www.wisegeek.com/what-is-a-milker-bill.htm.
164 Schweizer, Peter. 2013. Extortion: How politicians extract your money, buy votes, and line their

a remedy: typically, personal checks of around $11,000 from top execu-
tives to every committee member's campaign,[165] $100,000 institutional
checks to a Super PAC for relatively easy votes, or around $1 million for
tough votes that awaken constituent opposition. Then the operatives
dispense the dollars to their polling, messaging, and media partners,
and take their cut. The polling, messaging, and campaign money
elect compliant lawmakers in a numbers-driven process that is divided
among four or more entities along the pipeline.

The first contractor retained by political strategists is the
DATABASE firm. The left establishment uses Vote-Builder and the
right uses Data Trust, among others.[166] Both databases include nearly
all 240 million eligible voters in the country, including the ~151 million
most likely to vote in 2020.[167] They profile them based on state voter
registration information: who they are, where they live, and how they
label their politics—about 25% registered Republicans, 35% registered
Democrats, and 40% independents who decline to state.[168]

Second is the DATA ENRICHMENT firm. Catalist serves progressives, while i360 serves conservatives and libertarians, for example.[169]
They are "big data" companies. They have powerful computers with
data on almost *everything* about almost *everyone*. They know every digital
move you and we make: where we buy our socks, whether we invest in
stocks, our addictions to Starbucks, our fashion statements and invoices,
and whether we've adopted our children, a cat, a cause, or a candidate.
The voter data is *enriched* with hundreds or thousands of data points that
track most everything about most every prospective voter everywhere.

Third is the DATA ANALYST. He or she looks at the enriched
voter data, and with the help of smart computers, figures out what to
do with it to serve the interests of a client. This includes categorizing

---

own pockets. New York, NY: Houghton Mifflin Harcourt.
165 This is the maximum allowable contribution ($2,800 for the primary and $2,800 for the general
election from each partner in a married couple). See additional contribution limits at: https://www.fec.
gov/help-candidates-and-committees/candidate-taking-receipts/contribution-limits/.
166 See https://www.votebuilder.com/ and https://thedatatrust.com/.
167 According to Citizen Data's database which includes 186 million registered voters as of December
3, 2019.
168 Gallup. 2019. "Party Affiliation." Accessed November 18, 2019. https://news.gallup.com/
poll/15370/party-affiliation.aspx.
169 See https://www.catalist.us/ and https://www.i-360.com/.

every voter as digital *personas* they can use to help protect their clients from unmanaged change. A digital persona isn't exactly a person. It's more like a bound-up group of people held together by a stereotype. The data analyst discovers patterns of behavior common to the people who reflect each persona. Bill's persona, for example, buys two Starbucks matcha lattes every day, orders the salmon entrée every time, reflexively buys modern furniture online after viewing the same ad 20 times, and contributes to *any* organization or politician who supports a revenue-neutral price on carbon. There are, it turns out, millions of people who behave just as predictably as he does. Data analysts predict what we will do when presented with a set of choices, and enhance the data by making cause-and-effect clear to marketers.

Fourth is the MARKETING COMMUNICATIONS firm. There are hundreds of these, most working only for the red or the blue. There is no purple tower—choosing one is punished as betrayal if you're an entrenched interest. Each communications firm tests, refines, and rolls out messages to target voter personas like you and me, via the channels most likely to reach us at the right time and place—a Google search, Amazon purchase, Walmart visit, Starbucks boost, or Fox News bloviation, among others—and triggers us to act as the analysts predict.

Fifth is the CAMPAIGN CONSULTANCY. They design campaigns to elect candidates or promote policies favored by well-funded interest groups also often among their clients. Many top consultants offer their services for "free"—the privilege of engaging in the democratic process, plus the 15% commission on millions of dollars of media ad buys, and the side payments from interest groups, is reward enough.

Sixth is the MEDIA. On the right, the Republican *Pravda* and its predictable Wall Street sidekick pander to the right-wing base and then trap mainstream conservatives inside the same echo chamber. On the left, the politically-correct Democratic media play to the packaged prejudices of the progressive left and round up mainstream liberals so aghast at the extremist right that they don't challenge the righteous inside their echo chamber.

THE TWIN TOWERS OF THE DUOPOLY
How They Sell Policy Stability and Managed Change

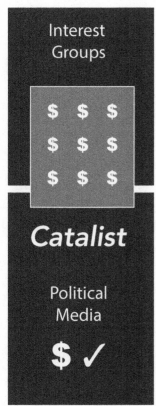

Interest
Groups

Catalist

Political
Media

$ ✓

Warrior Left

DATABASE
240M qualified to vote;
186M registered; ~151M
likely voting

DATA ENRICHMENT
300+ data points on
each voter

**DATA ANALYSIS
AND PREDICTIVE
MODELING**
Profile, Categorize, and
Predict voter behavior.

MESSAGE TESTING
A-B test messages and
measure behavior
by personae

**ONLINE
RECRUITMENT AND
SUPPORT BASE**
Roll out effective messages
- print, broadcast, cable,
social media.

**MEDIA – EARNED
AND PAID**
"Draw target viewers, sell
to advertisers.

**ON-THE-GROUND
MOBILIZATION**
Register and
Get-Out-The-Vote

Interest
Groups

datatrust

Political
Media

$ ✓

Warrior Right

The twin towers channel enormous amounts of money and power through their pipelines. The return on investment for those who operate the pipelines is quite generous. As much as $20 billion may flow to the political industry itself in 2020, to be divided among the lobbyists, pollsters, communicators, campaign professionals, and lawmakers. They deliver the audiences that the media industry sells in exchange for $240 billion per year in advertising.[170] The media in turn keeps consumers spending about $6 trillion per year for goods and services provided by the corporate, labor, and NGO clients who pay the political industry for protection and the media for marketing. Finally, the government spends about $4.7 trillion to fulfill their obligations to the entrenched service providers who have paid the political industry for protection.[171] About $3 trillion of that comes directly from taxpayers.[172] The other trillion-plus is borrowed from interest groups around the world—banks, nation-states, corporations, cartels, and wealthy families with massive capital holdings. Our children and theirs will repay it with their labor.

Paradoxically, the progressive and conservative bases unwittingly protect the creditors who loan the federal government the money to pay interest groups for delivering the services they demand from government. They do this by each demanding that one tower take down the other. In the false belief that total political victory by either the right or the left will sweep away the problems that concern them. Progressive fundamentalists want to take down the corporatist REPUBLICAN LLC tower, to liberate the oppressed victims of corporate capitalism and provide the people with the free stuff they think only government can provide. Conservative fundamentalists want to take down the statist DEMOCRATIC LLC tower, to liberate the persecuted victims of

170 Statista. 2019. "Media Advertising Spending in the United States from 2015 to 2022 (In Billion U.S. Dollars)." Accessed November 20, 2019. https://www.statista.com/statistics/272314/advertising-spending-in-the-us/.
171 OMB (Office of Management and Budget). 2019. "President's Budget." Accessed November 20, 2019. https://www.whitehouse.gov/omb/budget/.
172 Amadeo, Kimberly. 2019. "FY 2019 Federal Budget: Trump's Budget Request." The Balance, August 8, 2019. https://www.thebalance.com/fy-2019-federal-budget-summary-of-revenue-and-spending-4589082.

socialist statism and free people to enjoy the prosperity they think only corporations can provide.

What the fundamentalists miss is that statism and corporatism are the same thing. Using one half of the duopoly to take down the other is futile. It further entrenches both, until economic, social, and environmental forces of change grow irresistible, and the two formally unite as one—a corporate state that promises what both fundamentalists demand, in exchange for authoritarian control.

By playing their predictable roles as arch enemies, the progressive and conservative fundamentalists serve as useful idiots for the Democratic and Republican political industries. They keep the public divided into two separate political chambers—the left inside the blue tower, guarded by justice warriors, the right inside the red tower, guarded by freedom warriors. Outside the towers are the largest citizen group, the independents who can't vote in the partisan primaries that choose the only viable candidates. The result is a democracy divided and conquered, and a political class they reigns unchallenged.

We and a number of friends are pursuing a simple solution to disrupt this unfortunate turn of events, however. We call it In This Together. It was conceived by about 20 concerned Republican donors meeting as the Donor Roundtable, and we have now combined forces with independents and Democrats equally committed to democracy and the earth. Our plan is *not* to destroy the twin towers, or to demand change from them. We intend to disrupt their duopoly as we've begun to in California, by constructing a third tower between them, supported by a purple political infrastructure that serves the 67% of Americans left-to-right whose money and power is held hostage by the duopoly.

The third tower will not be a political party. The duopoly takes that option off the table. Instead, the third tower would connect the right and left halves of the 67% inside and outside the major parties who are disenfranchised by the system. That will shift the balance of political rhetoric from the extremes to the broad center, and restore the power of the real majority to lead authentic change, empowered and bounded by the Constitution, not vested interests and the political class.

THERE ARE TEN STEPS TO THIS PLAN.

First, get to know every voter in America—all 240 million of us—plus at least 30 million other marketplace and cultural influencers. Rather than knocking on doors, which could be tedious, we're doing this by compiling our own national voter and influencer list, and correlating it against the disturbing amount of personal information the Duopoly has on us. We may as well use it *for* us rather than just *against* us, we've rationalized. We have a trustees board to keep us on track, just in case.

Second, we are recrafting questions we used in campaigns to date, to find when voters will break ranks to elect problem-solvers. We will update these, test them in focus groups, then ask them in state and national surveys. Using advanced statistical analysis we will confirm which combination of questions in fact accurately predicts a voter's willingness to bridge the divide.

Third, we are using a cornucopia of consumer data and a voter database to extrapolate our findings to all voters, identifying millions of potential Solution Citizen voters, including decisive voters in key districts who, with high confidence, could be persuaded to swing.

Fourth, we are reaching out to our most likely allies, with messages they are most likely to hear, inviting them to join us. Direct mail and social media have proven most cost-effective to date, but communications tools change constantly, so we will need to stay current.

Fifth, we will recruit the five million most dedicated problem-solvers to take action in support of bipartisan environmental solutions and democracy reforms.

Sixth, we will reach out every week to as many as five million prospective or confirmed supporters, constantly improving the quality of our base, and growing it toward 15 million, the number our strategists believe can mobilize not just our voter coalition but our wider cultural base.

Seventh, partnering with dozens of local, state, and national bridge-building groups, we will cultivate authentic citizen communities capable of solving problems in their areas.

Eighth, we will begin to elect a Congress and more state legislatures that will enact *bipartisan* solutions combining the wisdom of the Protectors and the Liberators, regardless of what party, if any, holds a majority.

Ninth, we will bring into the White House women and men of high caliber, pragmatic idealists who will help make us safe, free, prosperous, whole, and proud.

Along the way, we will end this war, restore democracy, and save the planet, for all humankind.

CHAPTER 14

IN THIS TOGETHER

A DECLARATION OF INTERDEPENDENCE

Since the first Earth Day fifty years ago in 1970, the dominant narrative for environmental activism has cast crusading citizen heroes against profit-hungry corporate villains in an all-out war to save the earth.

The war narrative has bases in fact. Corporations can do great harm. The massive oil spill that turned Santa Barbara beaches black and the burning chemicals that engulfed the Cuyahoga River in thick smoke and iridescent flames, both in 1969, helped drive public demand for the federal Clean Air and Clean Water Acts in the 1970s, and set the filthy water mark for generations of battles. But since then, while the media weapons-makers of political warfare have thrived, policy has gridlocked, spending has exploded, debt has deepened, and the planet's oceans, forests, and climate have suffered a steady decline toward catastrophe.

We understand—we all feel deep and justifiable anger toward people and interest groups that have wronged us. Each of us has engaged in battle with people and companies who lied, cheated, and stole elections from us. We want to stop them from every harming us or anyone again. We *can't* easily see them as decent human beings—we're not sure they're human at *all*. There's something inside us that wants us to make them suffer for their wrongs. These feelings come over us before we're even aware, and they can be so intense we may have trouble setting them aside even when we know they are not helpful. When someone triggers our fear and hate, it can come tumbling out. That in itself can be scary. We may not want to face the demons inside that are raging at the demons outside.

But now, nearly all those demons are friends. We see them in a different light. We understand the convoluted logic that justifies evil in times of war. We know how much we have accomplished, for people and the planet, by sitting down with them in respect, to listen, hear, and learn.

It's not easy—we both know it. It requires practice—we've been there. It's simpler to look virtuous by attacking someone we fear, than to be virtuous by engaging them as another imperfect human being, and considering the slight possibility they have some hidden virtue to share.

But this is a test we can't afford to fail. We have a choice: succumb to fear, intensify the war, deepen the demonization, polarize the public, entrench the opposition, enrich the media, overstretch the economy, and degrade the air, water, ocean, forest and climate systems that support life on earth. Or balance fear-and-demonization with a faith that inside nearly every human being is something redeeming, and that courage and hope will enable the radical collaboration that gets us to the root cause of any problem.

Not everyone will rise above their fears. But you may be surprised how many will.

THE DONOR ROUNDTABLE 2019: REPUBLICANS BEGIN THE SHIFT

On April 26, 2019, twenty friends of ours gathered in a hot, noisy, crowded conference room near the center of Dallas. There, fortified with ample caffeine and all the rice and beans we could eat, we plotted the future of the planet.

Republican Senator Lindsey Graham spoke first. At dinner the prior evening, he and Democratic Senator Sheldon Whitehouse had together told of the dire consequences of using climate as a divisive wedge issue. This morning Senator Graham asked all of us to help end climate denial and return the GOP to its historical legacy as environmental problem-solvers.

Bill facilitated the five-hour discussion, while Trammell darted into and out of the meeting—he was entertaining the first of 177,236 other friends who would gather through the weekend for EarthX.

Strategists took turns explaining why Congress finds it virtually impossible to take sensible action to save the planet or resolve any hot-button controversy. It isn't Big Coal and Big Oil that stops them these days. It is Big Politics and Big Media, explained former food industry CEO Katherine Gehl, who with Professor Michael Porter leads research on the business of politics at Harvard Business School. The war for the planet is a cheap and easy way for political strategists to drive hard-left and hard-right voters to the polls, and for media companies to sell lookalike audiences to advertisers.

One solution, already tested and proven by our friend Charles Munger, Jr., is to give large and small donors an alternative to the duopoly. A distinguished physicist and an heir to the Berkshire-Hathaway fortune, Charles has begun to upend the particle physics of politics in California. Rather than channeling his dollars through the dominant partisan data platforms, he built his own, then channeled much of his $87 million in contributions through it. Instead of microtargeting voters with messages that drive fear and hatred for whatever "other" is an easy target, his data platform focused on an overlooked voter segment: "Solutions Voters" naturally inclined toward hope, optimism, and collaboration. By using big data to unite rather than divide voters, he built a bridge that shifted consistently shifted 17% of voters across the party divide to elect problem-solving candidates. His approach helped enable bipartisan supermajorities for the state's cap-and-trade climate program and other measures.

SOLUTION VOTERS:
A Rising Force in American Politics

Analysis by the Civil Society Institute,
based on data from Hart Research and V.J. Breglio, Inc.

Can Americans bridge the ideological divide and actually solve problems? For a fast-growing plurality of U.S. voters, the answer is "yes," according to research commissioned by the Massachusetts-based Civil Society Institute. Forty-three percent of us are "Solutions Voters" eager to reach across the aisle for collaborative solutions, according to data from bipartisan pollsters Hart Research and V.J. Breglio & Associates. Their survey of 1204 registered voters in August 2018 was part of a long-term expedition deep into the political wilderness to see if a bipartisan agreement of any kind has survived the onslaught of the past generation. It turned out that areas of left/right agreement are common in the wild, but rarely sighted in mainstream politics and media.

"Solutions Voters are more likely to vote against their preferred party and ideology to give support to the solutions they believe in," according to the institute's October 2018 report, Solution Voters: A Force in American Politics.

There is an emerging movement of voters working for a 'post-partisan' policy environment that starkly counters the hyper-negative partisanship that still engulfs the Democrats and Republicans and is reinforced by media reports that focus on outdated left/right analyses.

- **Solutions Voters and their informed optimism are an unrecognized constant force in American politics and embody the political DNA of unique American democratic values and principles.**
- **Solutions Voters are primed to move beyond polarized politics because they disrupt the left/right, conservative/liberal images we have of ourselves and our politics.**
- **Solutions Voters are not bound by political dogma. Therefore, they are more open to embrace solutions that arise from anyplace across the political spectrum.**
- **Solutions Voters most likely to vote against their preferred party and ideology to give support to the solutions he/she believes in.**
- **Political candidates who have the ability and courage to**

cross party dogma to offer the right mix to a solutions voter can hold special appeal to the Solutions Voter.

- Solution Voters are primed to be key to policy break-throughs on the following issues:
  - Health Care
  - Immigration
  - Criminal justice

Source: Solution Voters: A Force in American Politics. https://www.civilsocietyinstitute. org/SolutionsVoters.html: Civil Society Institute, Newtonville, MA, October 2018.

Scholars and pollsters had previously detected Solutions Voters, but no serious political strategist had systematically applied their findings to win elections, until Munger. The approach paid off, for both the environment and the economy. California is a national climate leader; its carbon pricing system cuts carbon emissions at a fraction of the cost of regulatory mandates.

Munger's model caused a stir. Most donors in the room had never veered from standard industry practice: get the hard-core base to the polls. Hope swing voters stay at home—they're too unreliable. Many of us couldn't believe there were that many swing voters, much less that we could earn their support by the quaint practice of solving problems.

By the end of the day, ten of us set a goal: build a national database platform as robust as Catalist for Democrats and DataTrust for Republicans. Design it to empower Solution Voters from across the 70% American center. Apply the Munger model to recruit the five million Solution Voters we need to gradually restore a working democracy with a governing majority that values freedom, justice, prosperity, and sustainability as indivisible.

The next year moved quickly. Five of us teamed with another donor alliance to build and deploy a new national database called Citizen, under the leadership of Mindy Finn, Kathryn Murdoch, and other cross-partisan leaders. With rich profiles of 270 million Americans, we were able to identify 45 million Solution Voters, ten times the number we will need to shift the business of politics. By January 2020, we began to put the tool to work. For the first time, we could donate to problem-solving candidates of either party, without supporting the divide-and-conquer tactics that threaten so much that is sacred to us.

Now we needed a campaign—something to remind Americans of what we used to read on every coin and currency, in the pre-Paypal era: *E Pluribus Unum*—from many, we are one. Our differences don't keep us apart. They bring us together and make us whole.

THE 2020 ROUNDTABLE: DONORS TARGET $1 BILLION FOR BIPARTISAN SOLUTIONS

A year after we gathered Republicans at that roundtable, we met again, but this time we invited Democratic and nonpartisan donors to join us in a grand experiment. It was April 24, 2020. The U.S. death toll from coronavirus had just topped 50,000 that morning. Americans were setting aside our divisions, at least a little, to fight the virus together. The timing seemed right. We'd been in plenty of rooms with billionaire Democrats or Republicans. But perhaps never before had 30 top donors from both parties gathered together to consider the unthinkable: join forces to fix democracy and protect the environment.

Working with more than a dozen democracy champions, business leaders, foundation chiefs, scientists, advocates, and political strategists, we laid out a bold plan called **IN THIS TOGETHER**, to begin to transform the business of politics in post-COVID America.

In political terms, we were proposing the campaign equivalent of a Soviet-American arms control deal: rather than wasting billions on endless political war, we could be citizens uniting with millions of others to the governing majority democracy requires.

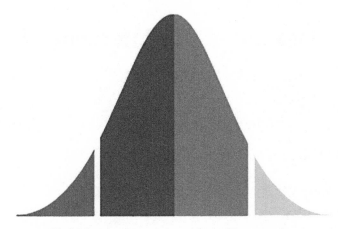

7 in 10 Americans are ready to solve problems together

At more than twice the cost of triggering ideologues, Solution Voters used to be expensive to identify and mobilize. But "big data" is changing that. With sophisticated predictive modeling, strategists can identify Solution Voters with 87% accuracy. By reaching a few thousand in a competitive district, we have defeated better-funded but more polarizing candidates.

On July 4, 2020—five weeks from the day we're writing this—we launched our campaign. The major media didn't take notice (we'd bet)—our story doesn't fit the profitable red-versus-blue narratives. But every day for the next four years, and for as long as it takes, you and we will reach more and more of America's 98 million politically homeless, especially the 45 million bridge-builders and 14 million problem-solvers. One-by-one, we will grow an active cross-partisan base of five million. We won't all agree, but we will declare our interdependence, and act on it. *E Pluribus Unum*— from many, we are one.

A Declaration of Our Interdependence
E Pluribus Unum

We're not all the same, but we are a family.

We don't always agree, but we are not at war.

From many, we are one, not in a melting pot,
but a complex social fabric.

They link us together and make us whole.

In a spirit of caring, connection, and creation, we embrace
four principles:

- **No Enemies** – we work through our conflicts to
  find solutions.
- **No Denial** – we face facts, discuss our differences,
  and resolve them.
- **No Excuses** – we each do our part – every citizen,
  leader, and business.
- **No Delay** – we each take action together, now.

We are all in this together.
Our differences are part of us.
Together, we are whole.

**Sign the Declaration at inthistogetheramerica.org,
earthx.org, or any of our partner sites**

IN THIS TOGETHER
RE-ENFRANCHISING THE 70%

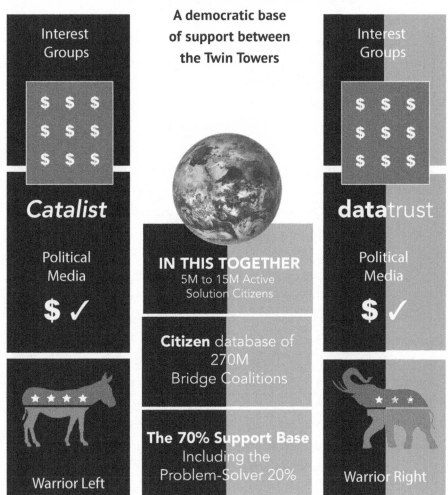

A democratic base of support between the Twin Towers

Interest Groups

$ $ $
$ $ $
$ $ $

Catalist

Political Media

$ ✓

Warrior Left

Interest Groups

$ $ $
$ $ $
$ $ $

datatrust

Political Media

$ ✓

Warrior Right

IN THIS TOGETHER
5M to 15M Active Solution Citizens

Citizen database of 270M
Bridge Coalitions

The 70% Support Base
Including the
Problem-Solver 20%

THE WISDOM OF THE RIVER

We live in a foreign land, radically different from the place our species grew up in, dislocated from our home of six million years. In this strange land, change is so fast that we find it difficult to take it all in, integrate with our inherited nature, and feel connected and whole.

The crisis we face is not merely economic or environmental. For the left, right, and many in between, the crisis is existential. We have the *feeling* something is wrong, and we interpret it according to our worldview, knowledge, experience, and politics.

The bipartisan strategy the two of us present in this book to end the war and save the earth may sound as mechanical and inhumane as the system we seek to transcend. But it reflects and reinforces a deep cultural shift long in the making, a reaction to the consumerist obsessions of 20th century industrialism that separated us, and a step toward reintegration.

No one better reflects the wisdom and purpose of the emerging culture of resolution, inclusion, optimism and faith than our friend Mark Dubois.

Mark is one of the bravest, truest, and most inspirational environmental leaders we know. He became famous to us way back in 1979, when he chained himself to the bedrock at the base of the Stanislaus River Valley, to prevent the Army Corps of Engineers from flooding the canyon by filling the New Melones Dam.[173]

Mark was genuinely ready to give up his life if, in so doing, he could help protect the life of that sacred canyon. But his greatest feat of bravery has been his mission in the years since. He has gently stood up to the fear, hate, and war mentality that so limits the effectiveness of environmental and social activism. He has weathered the skepticism and criticism of friends and colleagues who have told him his more collaborative approach lacks the power to overthrow the powers-that-be. We disagree. Mark's narrative doesn't fit with the hate-thy-enemy ethic of today's political media. But it stands the test of time, and can guide us along the path ahead.

Using Mark's words as our guide, we begin.

---

173 CBS News. 1979. "CBS News Report After Mark Dubois Chained Himself to a Rock." CBS News, May 25, 1979. Video, 2:28. http://www.stanislausriver.org/story/cbs-news-report-after-mark-dubois-chained-himself-to-a-rock-may-25-1979/.

THE "THROUGHLINE" THAT SAVES US FROM OUR PLANETARY CRISIS

By Mark Dubois

Our planet and our species in 2019 face a complex, multi-dimensional crisis. The severity and number of grave, intractable threats, among them global climate change, loss of global biodiversity, growing economic disparity and inequity, and looming food and water shortages can be overwhelming.

In the last 10,000 years, humankind hasn't faced a shared threat of this magnitude.

As a longtime river rafter, I'd liken our current situation to navigating Class V rapids, waters so dangerous that a slight misstep or misread of the currents can be catastrophic. To the untrained eye, Class V rapids appear to be hazardous chaos, yet with observation and experience, you can learn to identify the "throughline," the path that leads downstream past the most treacherous obstacles.

For the human race to survive and thrive, we must hone our skills at finding the throughline that gets us from the current crisis to a safer future for our children and grandchildren.

Here are three lessons we could learn from river rafting:

#1. Focus on the flow, not the obstacles

Presently, many hard-working environmental and social justice activists mobilize around "resistance" and fighting against an "enemy." Both my own experience and recent research confirms that such tactics postpone long-term progress: Outmoded strategies like fighting, blame, and demonizing "others" delay us from solving the current crisis—they're like fighting against a river's flow—and the river always wins.

Finding the throughline in Class V rapids demands full concentration and clarity of mind. If you obsess on obstacles, they become magnets, drawing you in, distracting you from the throughline.

Yes, President Donald J. Trump has rejected climate science and is an obstacle to change. But our current planetary crisis dwarfs even this President. In retrospect, we may see him as a galvanizing force who engaged more citizens around the world.

Water is powerful because it moves inexorably downstream. As a river rafter, I learned to move with it, even dance with it at times. As in Aikido, a Japanese martial art, it is vastly more effective and efficient to move with the flow than to thwart it.

For example, since the U.S. announced plans to withdraw from the Paris Climate Agreement in 2017, 25 governors representing 55 percent of the U.S. population and a $11.7 trillion economy—larger than all countries but the United States and China—formed the bipartisan United States Climate Alliance and committed to reduce their greenhouse gas emissions by 26-28% below 2005 levels by 2025. They have focused on where they are going, not what appeared to block them.

#2. Transform fear and anger into action

When there is a crisis on a river raft—lost oars, broken equipment, boat wrapped in a rock, , swimmers injured or in danger—rafters are forced to rely on new, previously untapped skills, talent, strength, and creativity. Panic doesn't serve. Paralysis can be fatal.

We reinforce a fear-based, self-fulfilling prophecy when we say, "I have no power" or "I have very little power" in response to the global crisis we all face. While there are limits to what one person can do, there is now mortal danger in denial, inaction and staying small. Many of us fear to ask and answer the question, "What is my role meant to be in these extraordinary times?".

Each of us is an activist, whether we know it or not. We activate the world around us with our spending, our attention or inattention, and our mental and spiritual focus — our fear, anger, goodwill, and love. Exploring how to grow, mature, and draw forth an activism grounded in mindfulness, connection, and kindness is vastly more effective than what we presently think of as activism. Mahatma Gandhi, Martin Luther King, Jr., Wangari Maathai, and Nelson Mandela embodied and enacted this most potent form of activism.

As Buckminster Fuller famously observed, small individual actions can function like the tiny trim tabs attached to the rudders of massive ships. That is, they initiate the change in direction.

Small, ultra-local choices made by millions of individuals in the course of their daily lives in conscious or unconscious collaboration with their neighbors have shifted and continue to shift our collective values. For example, the recent National Geographic film Paris to Pittsburgh celebrates how Americans from diverse backgrounds are developing real solutions to climate change. The accumulative effects of these actions are slowly changing humankind from a consumer species to a "restorer" species.

In my decades of experiences with concerned citizens and activists at home and across the globe, I've found that people yearn to be more engaged and effective, yet often cede their power to fear or anger. While fear and anger are important steps in moving beyond denial, the throughline we are looking for is found when we are rooted in clarity and love.

#3. Work with your raftmates

Our planetary crisis gives us the opportunity to align with what we hold sacred, including each other and the natural world. It invites us to transform our outmoded, fear-based, competitive, and disconnected consumer society into a vastly more sustainable, connected, and thriving one.

I've experienced such a possibility. As an International

Coordinator for Earth Day in 1990 and 2000, I had the privilege of watching people from across the globe collaborating: 200 million people in 141 countries in 1990 and another 200 million people in 184 countries in 2000. These events united more people around a common cause than any other global event in history. The synergy that can be unleashed when we work together profoundly moved me.

But what if the people who share our Earth and environment disagree with us? It is easy to hate the people who are paddling the opposite direction. Yet, even if we forget, we're in the same raft together. As enough of us do paddle in the right direction, our efforts have an effect and we automatically flow down the river.

For example, in 1979, I chained myself to a bedrock in California's Stanislaus River in an attempt to prevent the U.S. Army Corps of Engineers from flooding the canyon after they completed the New Melones Dam. My action came from a place of deep connection and love, not "fighting" or "resistance." The U.S. Army Corps was not my enemy. I simply could not turn my back on the life of the river and canyon, a sacred place that evolved over millions of years.

Although tens of thousands of people had organized alongside me to protect the Stanislaus River, we were unsuccessful. The canyon was eventually flooded and became a watery grave. While no one will ever again experience that beautiful and magical river, the vast outpouring of support for the Stanislaus and its tragic loss became a throughline to preserve other rivers. Our campaign, which led to decades of passionate grassroots activism, flowed into a growing national movement to preserve natural rivers.

When we operate from love—for our planet, our children and fellow human beings—and when our strategies and tactics emerge from there, we accelerate the speed of change, often in ways we can't foresee.

RADICAL TRANSFORMATION IS THE THROUGHLINE

Radical transformation of human attitudes and behavior has occurred repeatedly throughout history, including the systematic application of law (accompanied by a decline in personal violence), scientific discoveries that eliminated diseases, the abolition of slavery, women's suffrage, the U.S. civil rights movement, the fall of the Iron Curtain, the end of apartheid and more.

Yes, transformation can occur at a glacial pace. Sometimes, it appears to go backwards. However, it occurs nonetheless, and is presently unfolding all around us, often under the media's radar, since it adheres to none of the accepted narratives they recursively play.

Our evolution as a species created the riches and abundance of the modern world. It's been the engine of progress, including well-documented gains such as diminishing levels of human suffering, poverty and violence, with more education and spread of material wealth and health. Unfortunately, the costs of this progress have been extreme—our separation from the natural world, which we imagine to be a bank of 'resources' to be spent, and alienation from each other and ourselves—and now threaten our children's future.

As we anchor our hopes, dreams and actions in love, future generations will see this time as a turning point when we accelerated humanity's most profound evolutionary shift. How do we accelerate this shift? Seek the throughline and move toward it, own the power of your choices and actions, and know that there is no enemy to fight, save inaction and time itself. Heed this call as if your life depends on it. Because it does.

Mark Dubois (born February 24, 1949) began as an environmental activist initially focusing on saving rivers and has worked to mobilize citizens globally for a vibrant future. In 1972 he co-founded Environmental Traveling Companions (E.T.C.) to offer environmental education and Outward Bound-type trips to disabled persons and disadvantaged youth. In 1973, he co-founded *Friends of the River* to fight the flooding of the *Stanislaus River* and canyon by the *New Melones Dam. He reached national fame when he chained himself to the canyon's bedrock to prevent the river's flooding. He co-founded International Rivers* in 1984, and served as the International Coordinator of *Earth Day* 1990 and 2000. His personal papers from these organizations and other work from 1970–2002 are archived by the *Bancroft Library* at the *University of California, Berkeley.*

ABOUT THE AUTHORS

Trammell S. Crow is a Dallas-based Republican environmentalist, social impact investor, and commercial real estate developer who forgot to go back to his construction job in his 40s, instead raising four kids through college and engaging in civic, artistic, and environmental ventures before learning he had retired. In 2010, after recruiting business leaders to help shift Texas utilities from coal to cleaner energy, he unexpectedly gave birth to a fifth child known as *EarthX*. This latest offspring, now ten, has grown to become the world's largest environmental exhibition and conference, attracting 200,000 visitors to the EarthxFilm Festival, EarthxExpo, and EarthxCongress of conferences. Mr. Crow is a contrarian social investor, contributing to center-right conservation organizations, pro-environment Republicans, and Greenpeace. He serves on nonprofit boards such as Future 500, which brings corporations and activists together to actually *solve* environmental problems, and Million Acre Pledge, which commits individuals, businesses and foundations to conserve or restore large areas of bio-rich natural forests and irreplaceable ecosystems.

    Bill Shireman is a recidivist social entrepreneur, environmental policy innovator, and rare San Francisco Republican-in-plain-site. He brings together people who love to hate each other - capitalists, activists, conservatives, and progressives, among others. As President of the non-profit Future 500, he invites Greenpeace, Rainforest Action Network (RAN), ExxonMobil, Mitsubishi and other corporate and environmental leaders to slip into bed together to create, among other healthy offspring, the world's first corporate supply chain standards for sustainable forestry (between Mitsubishi, RAN, and then 400 other companies), the most effective beverage container recycling program (the California CRV deposit system and its progeny), and the 2008 agreement by both Greenpeace and Exxon-Mobil to support precisely the same federal tax on carbon, which went absolutely nowhere. So others can take up where he eventually leaves off, he teaches leadership and negotiations at the UC Berkeley Haas Business School, and serves as a surrogate founding father of BridgeUSA, where young progressives, conservatives, libertarians, and independents all register *decline-to-hate,* and engage in democracy by listening, speaking, learning, teaching, and then solving problems together. Professor Shireman is a prolific author who has written nearly as many books as he has sold. He has three children ranging in age from 13 to 29, none of whom plan to follow in his footsteps. They are making their own. He loves his wife Aileen Ichikawa, who seems to love him back, despite it all.

Made in the USA
Coppell, TX
22 December 2020